AQA GCSE Mathematics

Glyn Payne   Ron Holt   Mavis Rayment   Ian Robinson

Higher

Practice Book

www.heinemann.co.uk

✓ Free online support
✓ Useful weblinks
✓ 24 hour online ordering

01865 888058

Heinemann

Inspiring generations

Heinemann Educational Publishers
Halley Court, Jordan Hill, Oxford OX2 8EJ
Part of Harcourt Education
Heinneman is the registered trademark of Harcourt Education Limited

First published 2006

10 09 08 07 06
10 9 8 7 6 5 4 3 2 1

British Library Cataloguing in Publication Data is available
from the British Library on request.

10-digit ISBN: 0 435533 72 X
13-digit ISBN: 978 0 435533 72 4

Edited by Sarah Findlay
Typeset by Tech-Set Ltd, Gateshead, Tyne and Wear
Original illustrations © Harcourt Education Limited, 2006
Illustrated by Phil Garner
Cover design by mccdesign
Printed in the United Kingdom by Scotprint
Cover photo: Alamy Images ©

Acknowledgements
Harcourt Education Ltd would like to thank those schools who helped with the development and
trialling of this course.

The author and publisher would like to thank the following individuals and organisations for
permission to reproduce photographs:
Getty Images/Altrendo pp **19**; Alamy Images /Nature Picture Library pp **24**; Alamy Images/Tim Graham
pp **36**; Alamy Images/Photolibrary Wales pp **62**; Getty Images/PhotoDisc pp **87**; Alamy Images/TNT
Magazine pp **89**.

Every effort has been made to contact copyright holders of material reproduced in this book. Any
omissions will be rectified in subsequent printings if notice is given to the publishers.

Tel: 01865 888058   www.heinemann.co.uk   www.tigermaths.co.uk

1 Multiples, factors, powers and roots

Number   1

$4 \quad \frac{4}{3} \quad 9$
$2x^2 \quad a^2b$
□ △ ○

Exercise 1i

Links: 1A

> **What you should know**
>
> To get the square of a number, multiply it by itself. To get the cube of a number, multiply it by itself and then multiply again. Square roots and cube roots are the inverse of squaring and cubing.

 1 Work out the following, using the positive square root only in parts **(e)** and **(f)**.

(a) $4^2 + 5^2$

(b) $9^2 - 4^3$

(c) $\sqrt{49} + 5^3$

(d) $\sqrt{64} - \sqrt[3]{64}$

(e) $\dfrac{\sqrt{25} \times \sqrt{36}}{\sqrt{100}}$

(f) $\dfrac{11^2 \times \sqrt{16}}{\sqrt{36} - \sqrt[3]{8}}$

(g) $\dfrac{(15^2 - 13^2)}{(8^3 - 20^2)}$

(h) $\dfrac{\sqrt[3]{125}}{\sqrt[3]{1000}}$

Examples:

$2^2 = 2 \times 2 = 4$
$a^3 = a \times a \times a$
$\sqrt{25} = \pm 5$
because $5 \times 5 = 25$
and $-5 \times -5 = 25$
$\sqrt[3]{-27} = -3$

2 Ron said the answer to -5^2 is the same as $(-5)^2$. Is he right?

3 Which is the larger?

(a) 4^3 or $\sqrt{4225}$

(b) $\sqrt[3]{1.7}$ or 0.9^2

(c) $\sqrt{90}$ or $\sqrt[3]{3000}$

4 For each of the following, say which is possible and how many answers there will be, and then give the answer to 2 decimal places, if possible.

(a) -19^2

(b) $\sqrt{-126}$

(c) -0.8^3

(d) $\sqrt[3]{-287}$

(e) $\sqrt{1286}$

5 Evaluate the following, giving your answers to 2 significant figures.

(a) $3.6^2 + 4.9^3 - 2.8^2$

(b) $(5.2^2 - \sqrt{73})^2$

(c) $\sqrt[3]{476} - \sqrt{289}$

(d) $\sqrt{(8.2^2 \times 15.4^2)}$

Exercise 1ii

What you should know

To write a number as the product of its prime factors, use a factor tree or keep dividing by the smallest possible prime number.

To find the highest common factor (HCF), write each number as a product of prime factors and then multiply the factors common to both numbers.

To find the lowest common multiple (LCM), multiply the prime factors in both lists without duplication.

1 Write these numbers as products of prime factors. Give your answers in index form.

(a) 24   (b) 30   (c) 21   (d) 75   (e) 284

Example:
Prime factors of 18.

2 Which of the following numbers is a prime factor of both 78 and 104?

8   3   4   6   2   13   7   9

Example:
$2 \times 3 \times 3 = 2 \times 3^2$
Factors of 18 = $2 \times 3 \times 3$
Factors of 12 = $2 \times 2 \times 3$
HCF = $2 \times 3 = 6$
LCM = $2 \times 2 \times 3 \times 3 = 36$

3 Find the HCF of

(a) 24 and 60   (b) 75 and 90   (c) 30 and 72.

4 Find the HCF of

(a) 27, 45 and 108   (b) 72, 120, and 168.

5 From the list, choose two numbers with no common prime factors.

162   169   81   210   75   42

6 Two water containers have a capacity of 140 *l* and 126 *l*. I need to fill them both but can only use one jug, which is completely full of water. The jugs come in 6 *l*, 10 *l*, 14 *l* and 18 *l* sizes. Which jug should I use?

7 Find the LCM of

(a) 12 and 15   (b) 18 and 24   (c) 20 and 65.

8 Find the LCM of

(a) 9, 12 and 15   (b) 8, 22, and 40.

9 Ben barks every 48 s and Rex barks every 27 s. If they both bark at the same time, how long will it be before they bark at the same time again?

10 The north light flashes every 90 s and the south light flashes every 125 s. If they flash together, how long will it be before they flash together again?

Mixed Exercise

1 Work out the following.

(a) $3^3 + (-5)^2$ (b) $\sqrt{144} - 3^2$ (c) $15^2 + \sqrt[3]{64}$

2 Calculate the following. Give your answers to 1 decimal place, if necessary.

(a) $3.5^2 \times \sqrt{184}$ (b) $\sqrt[3]{-1.3} - 2.8^3$ (c) $\dfrac{(4.1 + 6.9)^2}{\sqrt[3]{240}}$

3 Write these numbers as a product of prime factors.

(a) 36   (b) 100   (c) 164   (d) 210

4 Find the HCF of

(a) 136 and 51   (b) 62 and 148   (c) 160 and 35.

5 Find the LCM of

(a) 54 and 72   (b) 63 and 28   (c) 18, 30 and 45.

Checklist

You should know about...	Grade	For more help, look back at Student Book pages...
squares, cubes, square roots and cube roots	D	1–2
how to find prime factors	C	3–4
HCF and LCM.	C	5–7

2 Fractions

Exercise 2i

Links: 2A–C

What you should know

You can find equivalent fractions by multiplying or dividing the numerator and denominator by the same number.

Fractions must have the same denominator before you can add or subtract them.

To compare fractions, change them into equivalent fractions with the same denominator.

1 Write the following in their simplest form.

   (a) $\frac{4}{12}$ (b) $\frac{12}{20}$ (c) $\frac{15}{90}$ (d) $\frac{120}{280}$

2 Put these in order, from smallest to biggest.

$$\frac{5}{8} \quad \frac{3}{5} \quad \frac{7}{10} \quad \frac{3}{4}$$

3 Work out

   (a) $\frac{3}{5} + \frac{1}{10}$ (b) $\frac{5}{8} - \frac{1}{12}$ (c) $1\frac{1}{2} + 2\frac{2}{5}$

   (d) $2\frac{1}{3} - 1\frac{5}{6}$ (e) $3\frac{3}{4} + 1\frac{2}{7} + 2\frac{9}{14}$ (f) $1\frac{3}{5} + 1\frac{3}{4} - 1\frac{5}{8}$

4 Frank had one piece of wood $2\frac{1}{2}$ m long and another piece $3\frac{1}{3}$ m long.

   (a) How much wood does he have altogether?

   (b) He uses $4\frac{3}{4}$ m of wood on a project. How much does he have left?

Example:

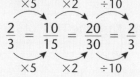

Exercise 2ii

Links: 2D

What you should know

To find a fraction of a quantity, remember that 'of' means 'multiply'.

1 Find $\frac{1}{2}, \frac{1}{3}, \frac{1}{4}, \frac{1}{5}$ and $\frac{1}{6}$ of £120.60.

2 There were 154 people at the cinema. $\frac{3}{7}$ were children. How many adults were at the cinema?

Example:

$\frac{2}{3}$ of 60 = $\frac{2 \times 60}{3}$

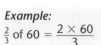

3 Which is larger?

   (a) $\frac{5}{6}$ of £48 or $\frac{3}{8}$ of £104   (b) $\frac{2}{3}$ of 2.1 kg or $\frac{5}{9}$ of 3.24 kg

4 During an endurance competition, competitors had to lie in icy water for as long as possible. Tom stayed in the water for $\frac{1}{6}$ of an hour and Ryan stayed in for $\frac{2}{3}$ of one-quarter of an hour. Who won?

Exercise 2iii

Links: 2E–G

> **What you should know**
>
> To find a reciprocal, invert the fraction.
>
> To multiply fractions multiply the numerators and multiply the denominators.
>
> To divide, change the sign into '×' and invert the fraction you are dividing by.

1 Find the reciprocal of

(a) $\frac{1}{2}$ (b) $\frac{5}{9}$ (c) 4   (d) $\frac{7}{3}$.

2 Work out the following, giving your answers in their simplest form.

Example:

Reciprocal of $\frac{1}{5} = \frac{5}{1}$ or 5

(a) $\frac{3}{8} \times \frac{2}{5}$ (b) $\frac{3}{4} \times \frac{5}{6}$ (c) $1\frac{3}{5} \times 1\frac{7}{8}$

(d) $1\frac{7}{9} \times 2\frac{1}{4}$ (e) $2\frac{2}{3} \times \frac{3}{5} \times 3\frac{3}{4}$ (f) $\frac{5}{8} \times 4 \times \frac{2}{5}$

3 Work out

(a) $\frac{4}{7} \div \frac{2}{3}$ (b) $\frac{3}{4} \div \frac{5}{6}$ (c) $\frac{3}{5} \div \frac{7}{10}$

(d) $\frac{3}{8} \div 5\frac{1}{4}$ (e) $2\frac{2}{3} \div 1\frac{7}{9}$ (f) $2\frac{3}{4} \times 1\frac{1}{3} \div 1\frac{5}{6}$.

4 Find the area of a carpet that is $3\frac{3}{4}$ m long by $2\frac{1}{5}$ m wide.

5 How many lengths of rope $\frac{5}{8}$ m long can I cut from a piece $6\frac{1}{4}$ m long?

6 A cuboid has a base that is $8\frac{1}{4}$ inches by $6\frac{2}{3}$ inches.

(a) What is the area of the base?

(b) The volume of the cuboid is $247\frac{1}{2}$ cubic inches. What is the height of the cuboid?

7 I spend $\frac{3}{8}$ of my allowance on a DVD and $\frac{2}{5}$ of what is left on a game.

(a) What fraction of my allowance did I spend on the game?

(b) If I have £4.50 left, how much was my allowance?

8 John puts $4\frac{2}{5}l$ of lemonade in a container. Their friends drink $2\frac{1}{2}l$, but Jay puts $3\frac{3}{4}l$ back in. They decide to sell the lemonade at 25p a glass. If the glass holds $\frac{1}{3}l$, how much money will they make?

⊞Mixed Exercise

1 Sally spends $\frac{1}{6}$ of her allowance on a magazine and $\frac{2}{5}$ on cosmetics. What fraction of her allowance does she have left?

2 Find $\frac{3}{5}$ of the following amounts.

   (a) £14   **(b)** 135 g   **(c)** 2.3 kg   **(d)** 1.02 *l*

3 If I travel $3\frac{1}{2}$ miles in $\frac{1}{4}$ of an hour, at what speed would I be travelling?

> Speed is found by dividing distance by the time taken.

4 Find the area of a circle with a radius of $3\frac{1}{2}$ inches.

> Use $\frac{22}{7}$ for π.

Checklist

You should know about...	Grade	For more help, look back at Student Book pages...
equivalent fractions and comparing fractions	E/D	9–12
adding and subtracting fractions	D	12–13
finding a fraction of a quantity	D	13–14
reciprocals	C	15–16
multiplying and dividing fractions.	C	14, 16–17

 **Exercise 3i**

Links: 3A–C

> ### What you should know
>
> To make a percentage, multiply by 100.
>
> To turn a percentage into a decimal or fraction, divide by 100.
>
> You can use percentages to compare amounts. To write one quantity as a percentage of another, first make a fraction and then convert to a percentage.

1 Copy and complete the following table of equivalent fractions, decimals and percentages.

Fraction	Percentage	Decimal
$\frac{3}{8}$		
		0.45
	64%	
$\frac{5}{9}$		
		1.625

Example:

15 as a percentage of 20
$= \frac{15}{20} = 0.75 = 75\%$

2 Place these in order, from the smallest to the largest.

     11% $\frac{3}{25}$ 0.109 $\frac{1}{7}$ 12.5%   0.124

3 Simon got 56 out of 75 in his art exam. Carl got $\frac{31}{40}$ in his. Who got the best result?

4 34 out of 172 students achieved an A grade in their maths exam. What percentage is this?

 **Exercise 3ii**

Links: 3D, 3E

> ### What you should know
>
> To increase or decrease a quantity by a percentage:
>
> *Method A*
> Work out the actual increase or decrease and then add it on to (or subtract it from) the original amount.
>
> *Method B*
> To increase, add the percentage to 100%. To decrease, subtract the percentage from 100%. Then, multiply the original amount by the new percentage.

1 Work out the following.

Amount	Increase by	Decrease by
160 g	**(a)** 12%	**(b)** 84%
2860 ml	**(c)** $32\frac{1}{2}$%	**(d)** 17%
7.25 km	**(e)** 4.6%	**(f)** $12\frac{1}{4}$%

Give your answers to 1 d.p.

2 McDougal's sold 7438 cups of coffee last month. This month sales are up by 11%. If a cup of coffee costs 99p, how much more money will they take on the sales this month?

3 A DVD player was advertised at £39.50 plus VAT. If VAT is $17\frac{1}{2}$%, what will be the total cost of the DVD player?

VAT = $17\frac{1}{2}$%

4 Sally decides to buy a car on credit. The car was priced at £4750 plus VAT. She had to pay a 22% deposit followed by 36 monthly payments of £172.50 each. How much more did Sally pay for buying on credit?

 **Exercise 3iii**

Links: 3G, 3H

> ### What you should know
>
> $$\text{Percentage change} = \frac{\text{actual change}}{\text{original amount}} \times 100\%$$
>
> $$\text{Percentage profit (loss)} = \frac{\text{actual profit (loss)}}{\text{cost price}} \times 100\%$$

1 The number of people taking golf lessons increased from 32 in 2004 to 44 in 2005. What is

    (a) the actual increase

    (b) the percentage increase?

2 A jacket cost £79. It was sold for £65. What is the percentage loss?

$$\text{Percentage loss} = \frac{\text{actual loss}}{\text{cost price}}$$

3 A bicycle was bought for £24.50. It was cleaned and polished, and then sold for £35. What is the percentage profit?

$$\text{Percentage profit} = \frac{\text{actual profit}}{\text{cost price}}$$

4 After a pay rise of 6%, an engineer earned £24 327. What did she earn before the pay rise?

Give your answer to the nearest pound.

5 A car depreciated (lost value) by 21% in a year. If it is now worth £3799, how much was it worth a year ago?

6 The house price index was 107.7 in May 2006 compared with a base index of 100 in May 2005.

(a) What was the percentage increase in house prices in that period?

(b) A house was valued at £180 000 in May 2005. What was its likely value in May 2006?

(c) A house was sold for £500 000 in May 2006. What was its likely selling price in May 2005?

Exercise 3iv

Links: 3I

What you should know

To work out repeated percentage change, add (or subtract) the percentage rate to (from) 100%, convert to a decimal and then multiply the original amount by the number of repeats given in the question.

1 Tom invests £300 for 3 years at a rate of 4% compound interest. How much does he have at the end of

(a) year 1   (b) year 2   (c) year 3?

Examples of repeated percentage change include compound interest and population changes.

2 Credit card companies charge compound interest each month on money borrowed. A silver card charges 5.9% per month and a green card offers 0% for 6 months, followed by 16.2% per month. If I borrow £2400 for 10 months, what is the difference between the interest charged by the two credit card companies?

In this question, interest is calculated *per month*.

3 How long will it take for the population of Crownborough to exceed 200 000 if the population is now 155 000 and the rate of increase is 5% per year?

4 If £430 grows to £652.77 in 4 years, what is the rate of compound interest?

Mixed Exercise

1 A box of 144 oranges contains on average three rotten fruit. What percentage is this?

Give your answer to 1 d.p.

2 The cost of a holiday to Spain has fallen by 16% over the last 3 years. If the cost was originally £240, how much does the holiday cost now?

3 How much VAT will I have to pay on a television costing £249 before VAT?

4 The cost of a scooter has fallen from £186 to £173. What is the percentage reduction in cost?

5 During an illness, a boy's weight fell by 6%. He now weighs 58 kg. What did he weigh before?

Give your answer to the nearest 100 g.

6 The amount of moorland in a part of Yorkshire is decreasing by 3% per year. If there is an area of 1024 km² now, how much will there be in 8 years' time?

Checklist

You should know about...	Grade	For more help, look back at Student Book pages...
conversions between fractions, decimals and percentages	C	20–22
writing one quantity as a percentage of another	C	23–24
percentage increase and decrease including VAT	C	24–28
percentage change including profit and loss and price index	C	28–31
reverse percentages	B	31–33
repeated percentage change.	C	33–36

Exercise 4i

Links: 4A, 4B

> **What you should know**
>
> Angles on a straight line add up to 180°. Angles round a point add up to 360°. Vertically opposite angles are equal.
>
> Corresponding angles are equal. Alternate angles are equal. Co-interior angles add up to 180°.

Calculate the size of the angles marked with letters. For each one, give a reason for your answer.

Example:

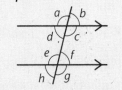

$a = e$, $b = f$, $d = h$, $c = g$
(corresponding angles)
$c = e$, $d = f$ (alternate angles)
$(c + f) = (d + e) = 180°$
(co-interior angles)

1

2

3

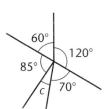

4

5

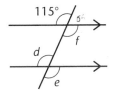

6

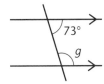

7

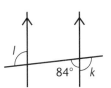

8

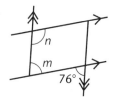

9

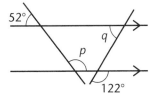

Exercise 4ii

Links: 4C

> **What you should know**
>
> Three-figure bearings are measured from north, in a clockwise direction and always have three digits.

1 For each diagram, work out the bearing of T from S and then the bearing of S from T.

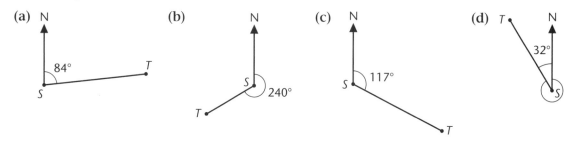

2 (a) Draw a representation of the following journey as accurately as you can.

A ship leaves port on a bearing of 125°. It travels on this course for 35 km and then changes to a bearing of 030°. It maintains this course for 40 km before changing to a course of 255° for 20 km.

> Start by marking a point P (the port) on the left-hand side of your page and drawing in a north line vertically up the page. Use the scale 1 cm = 5 km.

(b) Draw a line joining the final position of the ship to the port. What is the distance of the ship from the port and what bearing would the ship need to follow to return directly to port?

Exercise 4iii

Links: 4D, 4E

> **What you should know**
>
> The sum of the angles in a triangle is 180°. The exterior angle is equal to the sum of the two opposite angles.

For each of the following, find the lettered angles.

1
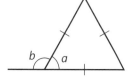

2
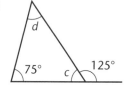

3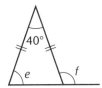

4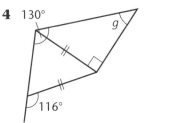

5

6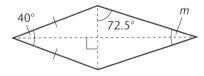

7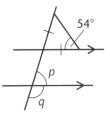

8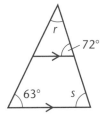

9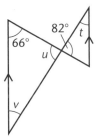

Exercise 4iv   Links: 4F

> **What you should know**
>
> Quadrilaterals are polygons with four sides. The interior angles add up to 360°.

1 For each of the following pairs of shapes, list the properties they have in common and the properties that are different.

(a) Square and rhombus.

(b) Rectangle and parallelogram.

2 Write down the names of all the quadrilaterals with these properties.

(a) Only one pair of parallel sides.

(b) Diagonals are equal in length.

(c) Only one pair of opposite angles are equal.

(d) Two pairs of adjacent sides equal.

(e) Diagonals meet at right angles.

Exercise 4v

Links: 4G

What you should know

The sum of the exterior angles of a polygon is 360°.

The sum of the interior angles of a polygon is given by the following formula:
$(n - 2) \times 180°$, where n is the number of sides of the polygon.

Calculate the size of the angles marked with letters.

1
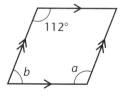

2
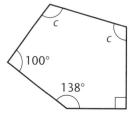

A regular polygon has all its sides and angles equal, so:

the exterior angle .

$$= \frac{360°}{\text{number of sides}}.$$

3
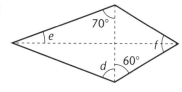

4
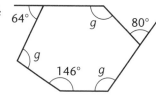

5
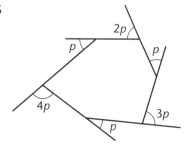

6
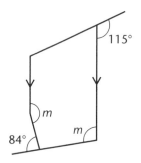

7 Calculate the sum of the interior angles of a regular polygon with 13 sides.

8 A regular polygon has an exterior angle of $22\frac{1}{2}°$. How many sides does it have?

9 Calculate the interior angle of a regular polygon with 24 sides.

10 Only part of a regular polygon is visible. If it has an interior angle of 156°, how many sides does the polygon have?

Mixed Exercise

Calculate the size of the angles marked with letters.

1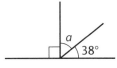

2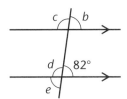

3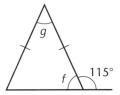

4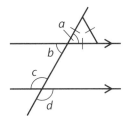

5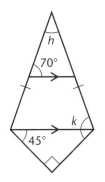

6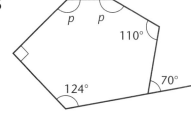

7 (a) Allport is 45 km on a bearing of 320° from Kingston. Make a scale drawing to show this.

  (b) What is the bearing of Kingston from Allport?

8 Which quadrilaterals have only opposite angles equal?

9 Calculate the size of an interior angle of a regular polygon with 22 sides.

Checklist

You should know about...	Grade	For more help, look back at Student Book pages...
properties of angles, including angles in parallel lines	D	39–44
bearings	D	45–47
properties of triangles	D	47–51
properties of quadrilaterals	D	51–53
interior and exterior angles of polygons.	D/C	53–57

5 Equations and inequalities

Exercise 5i
Links: 5A

> **What you should know**
>
> A simple equation is one involving an unknown letter. Solve simple equations by treating both sides in the same way. What you do to one side of an equation, you must do the same to the other side.

1 Solve

 (a) $x + 5 = 9$ (b) $d + 4 = 12$ (c) $e + 12 = 32$

 (d) $n - 7 = 4$ (e) $12 = z + 11$ (f) $50 = 100 - t$

> Write the letter on the left-hand side of the equals sign in your answers.

2 Solve these equations.

 (a) $6q = 12$ (b) $3t = 15$ (c) $5p = 30$

 (d) $4x = 24$ (e) $7y = 28$ (f) $9u = 63$

3 Find the value of the letter in each of these equations.

 (a) $\dfrac{a}{3} = 4$ (b) $\dfrac{k}{2} = 10$ (c) $\dfrac{g}{6} = 4$ (d) $\dfrac{h}{11} = 2$

 (e) $\dfrac{m}{8} = 5$ (f) $60 = \dfrac{n}{10}$ (g) $7 = \dfrac{x}{3}$ (h) $13 = \dfrac{y}{2}$

Exercise 5ii
Links: 5B

> **What you should know**
>
> To solve some equations, two operations are necessary before the solution is found. Again, you must treat both sides of the equation in the same way.

1 Solve the following equations.

 (a) $4a + 2 = 14$ (b) $3x + 4 = 10$ (c) $2m + 7 = 13$

 (d) $7p - 3 = 11$ (e) $9y + 4 = 31$ (f) $5t - 8 = 12$

> Write the letter on the left-hand side of the equals sign in each case. Equations involving a multiplication can be 'undone' by dividing both sides by the multiplication factor.

2 Solve

 (a) $\dfrac{u}{2} + 5 = 9$ (b) $\dfrac{h}{7} - 7 = 2$ (c) $\dfrac{x}{4} + 12 = 13$

 (d) $\dfrac{a}{6} - 10 = 0$ (e) $6 + \dfrac{e}{3} = 8$ (f) $19 - \dfrac{g}{8} = 8$

> Equations involving a division can be be 'undone' by multiplying both sides by the denominator (i.e. the value on the bottom of the fraction).

3 Solve the following equations.

 (a) $\dfrac{3w - 3}{9} = 1$ (b) $\dfrac{10t + 6}{3} = 12$ (c) $\dfrac{11 + 4x}{5} = 11$

 (d) $\dfrac{20 + 5c}{7} = 10$ (e) $\dfrac{7h - 22}{3} = 2$ (f) $\dfrac{8i - 20}{12} = 3$

> Remember to write the unknown letter on the left-hand side.

Exercise 5iii

Links: 5C

What you should know

Solutions of equations can be a negative value, a fraction or a decimal.

1 Solve the following equations, giving your answers as fractions.

Unless the question asks for a particular type of answer, you can give your solution as either a fraction or a decimal.

(a) $6s + 3 = 12$

(b) $16m - 1 = 1$

(c) $12q - 5 = 7$

(d) $9y + 3 = 17$

(e) $5 + 24i = 20$

(f) $21j - 2 = 7$

2 Solve the following equations, giving your answers as decimals.

(a) $8w - 6 = 4$

(b) $5e + 4 = 13$

(c) $6g + 7 = 70$

(d) $8l + 16 = 17$

(e) $5n - 11 = 30$

(f) $12 + 4p = 15$

3 Solve these equations.

(a) $4e + 15 = 3$

(b) $8z + 20 = 4$

(c) $2m + 30 = 6$

(d) $5c + 45 = 5$

(e) $6p + 50 = 8$

(f) $9l + 180 = 90$

4 Solve the following equations.

(a) $\frac{m}{2} + 5 = 3$

(b) $\frac{f}{3} + 7 = 8$

(c) $\frac{h}{5} - 9 = -10$

(d) $\frac{n}{4} - 3 = -7$

(e) $\frac{x}{3} + 2 = -1$

(f) $\frac{a}{5} - 5 = -9$

Exercise 5iv

Links: 5D

What you should know

When there are unknowns on both sides of the equation, collect like terms on one side only before solving. Often, more than two steps are involved.

1 Solve the following equations.

Always subtract the smaller value of the unknown from the larger value of the unknown as your first step.

(a) $2x + 7 = x + 10$

(b) $4t + 8 = 3t + 13$

(c) $12a + 4 = 8a + 16$

(d) $7y + 2 = 13y - 4$

2 Solve the following equations.

(a) $5q + 5 = 2q - 4$

(b) $4a + 2 = 3a - 2$

(c) $15w + 10 = 12w + 7$

(d) $5m + 3 = 7m - 15$

Exercise 5v

Links: 5E

What you should know

You need to read the problem carefully before you set up an equation. Solve it using the methods introduced in Chapter 5.

1 Three numbers are given by the expressions $p + 8$, $3p + 1$ and $5p - 4$. The sum of the numbers is 77. Find the three numbers and say what type of numbers they are.

2 The perimeter of a parallelogram shown here is 18 cm.

Formulate an equation in terms of x and solve it to find the length of the sides of the parallelogram.

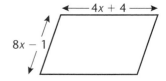

3 Tom thinks of a number, muliplies it by 3 and adds 7. His answer is 5. Write an equation for this puzzle. What was his original number?

4 The sum of three consecutive numbers is 192. Find the three numbers.

5 PQ is a straight line. Find the value of x and the angles shown in the diagram.

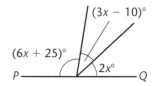

Exercise 5vi

Links: 5F

What you should know

Simultaneous equations can be solved by the method of elimination. Eliminate one of the unknowns by adding or subtracting the equations.

1 Solve the simultaneous equations.

(a) $a + b = 15$	(b) $2x + y = 10$	(c) $2c + b = 7$
$a - b = 5$	$x - y = 2$	$-2c + 8b = 2$

If the x or y values have the same numerical value but differ in sign, you add, or if they have the same sign, you subtract.

2 Solve the simultaneous equations to find values for the two unknowns.

(a) $11x + y = 15$	(b) $3w + 2v = 16$	(c) $6p - 3q = 3$
$5x + y = 9$	$w + 2v = 12$	$10p - 3q = 11$

3 Find the values of the unknowns in the following simultaneous equations.

(a) $4e - 5f = 14$	(b) $7g - 3h = 2$	(c) $12i + 2j = 14$
$2e - 2f = 8$	$2g + 3h = -11$	$7i + 2j = 4$

4   Solve the following simultaneous equations.

   (a) $3x + 2y = 12$ **(b)** $3a + b = 14$ **(c)** $5k - 3l = 7$
              $2x - y = 1$ $a + 5b = 14$ $4k + 2l = 10$

5   Solve these simultaneous equations.

   (a) $4d + 3e = 3$ **(b)** $9x + 5y = 6$ **(c)** $5r - 6s = 2$
              $3d + 2e = 3$ $3x - 2y = -9$ $2r - 2s = 0$

6   Solve these simultaneous equations.

   (a) $3y + 5x = 9$ **(b)** $6g + h = 8$ **(c)** $2p - 8q = 0$
              $-2y + 7x = 25$ $4g + 3h = 3$ $5p - 6q = -7$

7   The sum of two numbers is 69 and the difference is 15. Find the two numbers.

> Call the unknown number by a letter, say n.

8   The rail fare for one adult and one child is £17, and the fare for two adults and three children is £39. Find the cost of each type of fare.

Exercise 5vii

Links: 5G

What you should know

An expression in which the left- and right-hand sides are not equal is called an inequality.

1   Write the correct inequality between these pairs of numbers.

   (a) $-6, -13$ **(b)** $2.7, 2.6$ **(c)** $0.010, 0.011$

> $<$ means 'less than'.
> $>$ means 'greater than'.
> $\leqslant$ means 'less than or equal to'.
> $\geqslant$ means 'greater than or equal to'.

2   Write down the whole number values of the letter that satisfy the following inequalities.

   (a) $m < 6$ and $m \geqslant 1$ **(b)** $x \leqslant 2$ and $x \geqslant -1$

3   Write each pair of inequalities given in Question 2 as a combined inequality.

4   Draw a number line between -5 and $+10$. Show the following inequalities on the number line.

   (a) $x \geqslant 4$ **(b)** $p \leqslant 9$

   (c) $d > -3$ **(d)** $-5 \leqslant a \leqslant -3$

> Use the symbol ○ when the end value is not included and the symbol ● when the end value is included.

5   Write down the values for each letter to 1 decimal place to satisfy the following inequalities.

   (a) $f > 9.9$ and $f \leqslant 10.2$ **(b)** $m \leqslant 0.3$ and $m \geqslant 0.1$

   (c) $t \geqslant 99.9$ and $t \leqslant 100.2$ **(d)** $-5.1 \leqslant q < -4.7$

Exercise 5viii

Links: 5H

> ### What you should know
>
> To solve equations involving inequalities you use exactly the same rules for algebra as ordinary equations. The balance method still applies.

1 Solve the following inequalities, where the letter has integer values.

    (a) $4t > 28$ **(b)** $8x \leqslant 32$ **(c)** $10b \geqslant 80$ **(d)** $3c < -15$

2 Solve the following inequalities, where each letter has integer values.

    (a) $4h + 4 > 16$ **(b)** $7m - 3 > 32$ **(c)** $8 + 5y < 28$

3 Solve the following inequalities. All the letters represent integer values. State the solution set clearly.

    (a) $4x \geqslant 7x - 12$ **(b)** $12w + 8 \geqslant 8w$

    (c) $10y - 18 \leqslant 5y + 7$

> There is usually more than one answer when you solve an inequality and you need to state all possible answers. This is called the 'solution set'.

4 Write down the solution set for each of the following inequalities. State the solution set clearly.

    (a) $20 < 5q \leqslant 45$ **(b)** $-8 < 8m \leqslant 48$ **(c)** $-18 \leqslant 6d < -12$

Exercise 5ix

Links: 5I

> ### What you should know
>
> When you divide (or multiply) by a negative number you must always remember to reverse the inequality sign.

1 Solve these inequalities.

    (a) $11 - 2a \geqslant 5$ **(b)** $17 - 3x \leqslant 2$ **(c)** $14 - 6p > 2$

    (d) $32 < 14 - 3q$ **(e)** $13 \leqslant 7 - 2y$ **(f)** $27 \geqslant 9 - 6f$

Mixed Exercise

1 Solve each of these equations.

    (a) $x - 5 = 6$ **(b)** $81 = 9y$

    (c) $14 = \dfrac{q}{3}$ **(d)** $22 - \dfrac{h}{5} = 16$

    (e) $\dfrac{6a - 2}{11} = 2$ **(f)** $4d + 6 = 2d + 14$

    (g) $y - 6 = 5y + 12$

> The solutions to the equations can be positive, negative, whole numbers, fractions or decimals.

2 The sum of three consecutive whole numbers is 141.
Find the three numbers.

3 The perimeter of an isosceles triangle is 39 cm. The base
length is $(2x - 1)$ cm and one of the other sides is
$(3x + 4)$ cm. Formulate an equation in terms of x and solve
it to find the lengths of the sides of the triangle.

4 Solve this simultaneous equation.
$$4f - 3e = 8$$
$$5f + e = -9$$

5 Write down the whole number values for each letter.
  (a) $y > 10$ and $y \leqslant 13$ **(b)** $d \leqslant -1$ and $d > -4$

6 Solve the following inequalities.
  (a) $3c - 6 \leqslant 9$ **(b)** $14 \geqslant 5 - 3g$
  (c) $20 < 4j \leqslant 36$ **(d)** $5q - 4 < 11q - 16$

Checklist

You should know how to...	Grade	For more help, look back at Student Book pages...
solve simple equations	D	60–62
solve equations combining two or more operations	D/C	62–63
solve equations that have negative, decimal or fractional answers	C	63–65
use equations to solve problems	C/B	66–68
solve simultaneous equations	B	68–72
write and solve inequalities, and represent them on a number line.	C	73–78

6 Measurements and approximations

Exercise 6i

Links: 6A–C

> ### What you should know
>
> To convert between metric units, use these conversions:
>
> 10 mm = 1 cm, 100 cm = 1 m
>
> 1000 g = 1 kg, 1000 kg = 1 tonne (t)
>
> 100 cl = 1000 cm^3 = 1 l
>
> To convert between metric and imperial units, use these conversions:
>
> | Metric | 8 km | 30 cm | 1 l | 4.5 l | 1 kg | 2.5 cm | 1 m | 25 g |
> |---|---|---|---|---|---|---|---|---|
> | Imperial | 5 miles | 1 foot | $1\frac{3}{4}$ pints | 1 gallon | 2.2 pounds | 1 inch | 39 inches | 1 ounce |

1 Find the total of the following lengths in metres.

0.42 km   15.8 m   3640 cm   15 200 mm

2 Peter walks 15 km and Sally walks $8\frac{1}{2}$ miles. Who walks further?

3 Mamet is replacing an old picture frame that measures 1 foot by 9 inches. All the frames now come in metric measurements. What size should he ask for?

4 Tom has a mass of 10 stone. An airline will only accept applications for cabin crew from people with a mass of less than 65 kg. Can Tom apply?

5 A recipe for biscuits uses 250 g of flour, 100 g of butter and 140 g of sugar. My scales only measure in ounces. Approximately how much of each ingredient do I need?

6 A field measures 3400 m by 6500 m.

(a) What is the area of the field in square metres?

(b) What is the area of the field in square kilometres?

1 m^2 = 10 000 cm^2

1 m^3 = 1 000 000 cm^3

7 A concrete pillar with a base area of 10 125 cm^2 and a height of 175 cm is to be made. How many cubic metres of concrete will be needed? Give your answer to a suitable degree of accuracy.

**Exercise 6ii**   **Links: 6D, 6E**

> ### What you should know
>
> You can round to any number of decimal places (d.p.) or significant figures (s.f.). The first s.f. is the first non-zero figure, reading from the left.
>
> To estimate an appropriate answer, round all of the numbers to 1 significant figure and do the calculation using these approximations.

1 Round 16.352 to

    (a) 1 d.p.   (b) 2 d.p.   (c) the nearest ten.

2 Round to 1 d.p.

    (a) 3.99   (b) 10.009   (c) 0.09

Examples:

26 818 is 27 000 to 2 s.f.
0.007038 is 0.007 to 1 s.f.

Significant figures are counted from the left.

3 Round 6 542 000 to

    (a) 1 s.f.   (b) 2 s.f.   (c) the nearest thousand.

4 The mass of an insect was given as 0.0837 g.
    What is this rounded to

    (a) 1 s.f.   (b) 2 s.f.   (c) 3 s.f.?

5 Use approximations to estimate the answers to

    (a) 532×392 (b) $4.36 \div 1.98$ (c) $\dfrac{(5.2)^2 \times 3.6}{3.8 \times 4.7}$.

6 Estimate the cost of 573 *l* of lemonade at 18p per litre.

Round each number to 1 s.f. to estimate the cost.

7 To form a roof, a joiner needs 87 lengths of timber 2.6 m long. If timber costs £2.34 per metre, estimate the cost of the wood for the roof.

Exercise 6iii   **Links: 6F, 6G**

> ### What you should know
>
> To convert a decimal or fraction part of an hour into minutes, multiply by 60.
>
> Use these formulae to find speed or density:
>
> $$\text{speed} = \frac{\text{distance}}{\text{time}}$$ $$\text{density} = \frac{\text{mass}}{\text{volume}}$$

1 Change

    (a) 5.1 h into hours and minutes

    (b) 3 h 12 min into hours.

2.6 hours
= 2 hours + (0.6 × 60) min
= 2 h 36 min

2 A train travels 325 miles in 3 h 15 min. What was its speed?

3 Jan walked for 2 h 24 min at an average speed of 5 km/h. Bill walked at a speed of 8 km/h for 1 h 45 min. Who walked further?

4 A whale swam 29.34 km in 2 h 20 min. Write the speed in metres per second, to the nearest metre.

5 A piece of wood has a density of 1.4 g/cm^3. What is the mass of a piece of wood with a volume of 180 cm^3?

6 A stone has a mass of 1.2 kg and a volume of 350 cm^3. What is the density of the stone in g/cm^3? Give your answer to 1 d.p.

7 A plastic sheet with a density of 0.08 g/cm^3 is made into a solid cylinder. If the cylinder has a radius of 8.4 cm and a height of 14 cm, what is its mass?

8 A cube of limestone, with sides of 9.5 cm, has a mass of 2.4 kg. A sphere of marble with a radius of 3.7 cm has a mass of 2.8 kg. Which material has the greater density?

Volume of sphere $= \frac{4}{3}\pi r^3$

Exercise 6iv

Links: 6H, 6K

What you should know

The minimum value is the lower bound. The maximum value is the upper bound.

Absolute error is the difference between the measured value and the nominal value. The nominal value is the value something is supposed to be.

1 Give the range of possible values for the following measurements.

(a) 9 ml (to the nearest millilitre)

(b) 53 cm (to the nearest centimetre)

(c) 4.7 m (to 1 d.p.)

(d) 7.93 min (to 2 d.p.)

Example:
5 cm measured to the nearest centimetre =
$4.5 \leqslant$ length < 5.5

2 If $p = 4.6$ g and $q = 2.3$ g, correct to 1 d.p., find the least and greatest possible values for the following equations.

(a) $p + q$ (b) $p - q$ (c) pq (d) $\dfrac{p}{q}$

3 If 3.24 m was cut from a piece of wire 15.49 m long, what is the greatest possible amount of wire left? Each measurement is correct to 2 d.p.

4 Dave ran 200 m in 82.4 seconds. If the track is measured to the nearest metre and the time to the nearest tenth of a second, what is the fastest possible speed of Dave's run?

5 A package is meant to have a mass of 3.4 kg. Its mass is 3.28 kg. Calculate the absolute error and the percentage error to 1 d.p.

Percentage error =

$$\frac{\text{absolute error}}{\text{nominal value}} \times 100\%$$

6 A circle has a radius of 4.5 cm, correct to 1 d.p.

(a) Find the least and greatest possible areas and the nominal area. Give your answers in terms of π.

(b) What is the maximum absolute error?

(c) Find the maximum percentage error.

Mixed Exercise

1 Polly's car can travel 11 miles on 1 *l* of petrol. How far will it travel on 1 gallon?

2 How long will a journey of 84 km take if I travel at an average speed of 40 km/h?

3 What would be the volume of a cube of material with a mass of 5.6 kg and a density of 0.65 g/cm^3?

4 A company produces 3480 toys at a total cost of £835.20. Estimate how much each toy cost to produce.

5 A rectangle is 11 cm by 7 cm, measured to the nearest whole centimetre. What is the smallest possible area?

6 A cube has a side length of 5.3 cm, measured to 1 d.p. What is the maximum percentage error in the volume of the cube?

Checklist

You should know about...	Grade	For more help, look back at Student Book pages...
conversion between units	D/C	80–83
rounding including significant figures	C	84–86
compound measurements	D/C	87–91
estimating using approximations	C	91–92
accuracy of measurement, limits and error.	C to A	93–100

Exercise 7i

Links: 7A, 7B

What you should know

The perimeter of a shape is the sum of the lengths of all its sides.

Area = $l \times w$

Area = $\frac{1}{2} \times b \times h$

Area = $b \times h$

Area = $\frac{1}{2} \times (a + b) \times h$

Area of a circle = πr^2.

Circumference of a circle = πd or $2\pi r$.

1 Find the area of the following shapes. All measurements are in centimetres.

(a)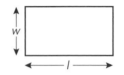

(b)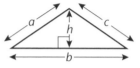

(c)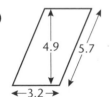

(d)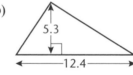

(e)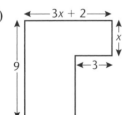

(f)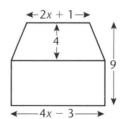

2 Find the perimeter of (a), (c), (d) and (e) in Question 1.

3 A triangle has an area of 22.4 cm². If the height is 7 cm, what is the length of the base?

4 Find the area of the following shapes.

(a)
←9 mm→

(b)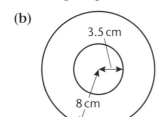
3.5 cm
8 cm

(c)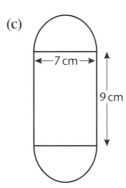
←7 cm→
9 cm

5 What is the perimeter of **(a)** in Question 4?

6 A counter has a circumference of 28.2 cm. What is its radius?

7 The area of a circular table top is 6362 cm². Calculate the circumference of the table top. Give your answer to a suitable degree of accuracy.

Exercise 7ii   **Links: 7C, 7F**

What you should know

Arc length $= \dfrac{\theta}{360} \times 2\pi r$.

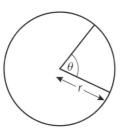
θ
r

Sector area $= \dfrac{\theta}{360} \times \pi r^2$.

Volume of a prism = area of cross section × length.

Area = sum of the areas of all its faces.

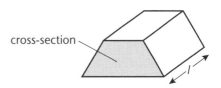
cross-section
l

1 Find the arc length and area of each of the following sectors.

(a)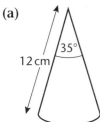
12 cm
35°

(b)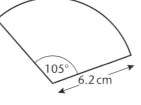
105°
6.2 cm

(c)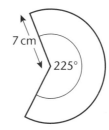
7 cm
225°

2 A sector has an angle of 40° at the centre and an area of 8.73 cm². Find:

   (a) the radius   **(b)** the arc length.

3 A sector has an arc length of 3.93 cm and an angle of 30° at the centre. Find the area of the circle from which it was cut.

4 Find the volume of the following prisms. All measurements are in centimetres.

(a)
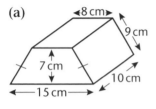

(b)
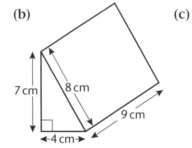

(c)
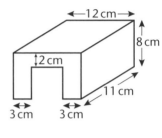

5 Find the surface area of the prisms in Question 4.

6 A 500 m*l* tin of paint covers 2 m². How many tins would be needed to paint this shape?

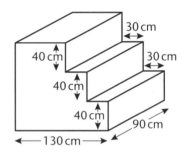

Exercise 7iii

Links: 7D, 7E

> ## What you should know
>
> The plan is the view from above. The side elevation is the view from the side and the front elevation the view from the front.
>
> A plane of symmetry divides a 3-D shape into two halves, where one half is the mirror image of the other half.

1 Draw a plan view, a front elevation and a side elevation (from the right-hand side) for each of the following.

2 Copy the following shape and show all the planes of symmetry.
Draw a separate diagram for each one.

Exercise 7iv

Links: 7G

> ### What you should know
>
> Volume of a cylinder = $\pi r^2 h$.
>
> Surface area = $2 \times \pi r^2 + 2\pi rh$ (2 circles + curved surface).
>
>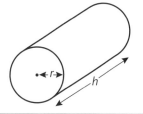

1 Find the volume of the following cylinders.

(a)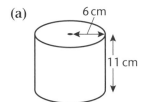

(b)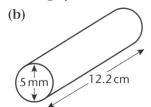

(c)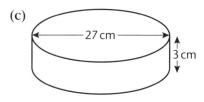

2 Find the surface area of each of the cylinders in Question 1.

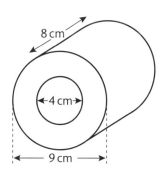

3 (a) Find the volume of this pipe made out of metal.

(b) If it was melted down and remoulded into a solid cylinder with a radius of 5 cm, what would be the height of the cylinder? (Assume that no metal is lost in the process.)

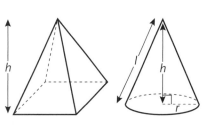

Exercise 7v

Links: 7H, 7I

> ### What you should know
>
> Volume of a pyramid = $\frac{1}{3}$ area of base $\times$ height.
>
> Volume of a cone = $\frac{1}{3}\pi r^2 h$.
>
> Surface area of a pyramid = sum of areas of each face.
>
> Surface area of a cone = area of base + area of curved surface = $\pi r^2 + \pi rl$.
>
> Volume of a sphere = $\frac{4}{3}\pi r^3$.
>
> Surface area of a sphere = $4\pi r^2$.
>
>

1 Find the volumes of the following.

(a)

11.5 cm

11 cm

7 cm

(b)

←6 cm→

12.4 cm

12 cm

(c)

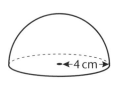

←4 cm→

2 Find the surface area of the shapes in Question 1.

3 The surface area of a spherical football is 804.25 cm². The curved surface of a cone has the same surface area.

(a) What is the radius of the base of the curve if the slant height is 24 cm and the perpendicular height is 20 cm?

(b) What is the difference in the volume of these two shapes?

4 In each of these formulae, *a*, *b* and *c* represent length. State whether each formula represents a length, area, volume or none of these. Explain your answer.

(a) abc **(b)** $3a + 4b$ **(c)** $b^2 + 3c^2$

(d) a^3c **(e)** $4\pi bc$

Mixed Exercise

1 Find the areas of the following shapes. All measurements are in millimetres.

(a)

25

14

12

17

(b)

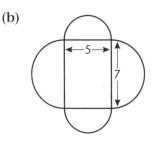

←5→

7

(c)

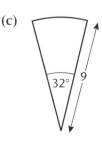

32°

9

2 Find the perimeters of the shapes in Question 1.

3 Find the angle at the centre of a sector with a radius of 9 cm and an area of 31.8 cm².

4 Draw diagrams to show all the planes of symmetry of a cuboid 7 cm by 4 cm by 2 cm.

5 Find the volume of the following. All measurements are in centimetres.

(a)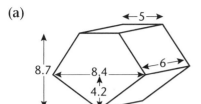

(b)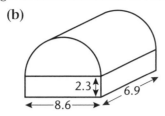

(c)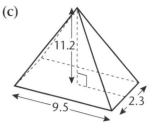

6 A cylindrical open-topped barrel contains 4021 *l* of water when full.

    (a) If the height of the water is 0.8 m, what is the radius of the base? Give your answer to 1 decimal place.

    (b) How high, to the nearest centimetre, would 1160 *l* reach?

    (c) What is the exterior surface area of the barrel?

7 The top 3 cm of a conical-shaped candle are removed, to make two candles instead of one. The candle was originally 8 cm high. Find

    (a) the volume of each candle

    (b) the surface area of each candle.

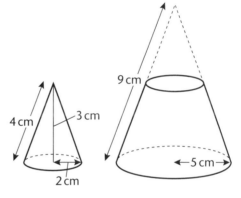

Checklist

You should know about...	Grade	For more help, look back at Student Book pages...
perimeter and area of a triangle, parallelogram, trapezium and compound shapes	D	102–105
circumference and area of circles	D/C	105–107
arc length and area of sectors	A	108–109
plans and elevations and planes of symmetry	D	110–112
volume and surface area of prisms	D/C	112–114
volume and surface area of cylinders	C	114–116
volume and surface area of pyramids and cones	A/A*	116–118
volume and surface area of spheres	A/A*	118–119
dimension theory.	B	119–122

8 Constructions and loci

Exercise 8i

What you should know

When using compasses you must leave the construction arcs as evidence that you have used the correct method.

Construct triangles with the following measurements.

1 Triangle *ABC* where *AB* = 10 cm, *AC* = 8 cm and *BC* = 6.5 cm.

2 Triangle *DEF* where *DE* = 9.5 cm, *DF* = 6.4 cm and *EF* = 8 cm.

3 Triangle *GHI* where *GH* = 8.7 cm, *GI* = 5.3 cm and *HI* = 6.6 cm.

4 An equilateral triangle of side 7.3 cm.

5 An isosceles triangle of sides 8.2 cm, 8.2 cm and 5.7 cm.

Exercise 8ii

What you should know

A perpendicular bisector cuts a line segment in half, and is perpendicular to the line segment.

The bisector of an angle divides an angle into two equal parts.

There are standard constructions for angles of 60° and 90°.

1 Construct
   (a) triangle *ABC* where *AB* = 7.5 cm, *AC* = 6.5 cm and *BC* = 5.5 cm
   (b) the bisector of angle *B*
   (c) the perpendicular bisector of *BC*.
   If these lines meet at point *P*, measure *AP*.

2 Construct
   (a) triangle *DEF* where *DE* = 9 cm, *DF* = 7 cm and angle *EDF* = 90°
   (b) the angle bisectors of angles *E* and *F*.
   If these lines meet at point *P*, measure *DP*.

3 Construct
   (a) an accurate copy of triangle *LMN*, shown in the diagram
   (b) the bisector of angle *M*
   (c) the perpendicular from *N* to side *LM*.
   If these lines meet at point *P*, measure *LP*.

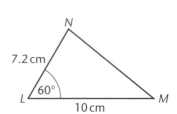

4 Construct an accurate copy of this quadrilateral.

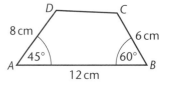

(a) Start by drawing AB = 12 cm.

(b) Construct an angle of 90° at A then bisect it to give an angle of 45°.

(c) Measure AD = 8 cm.

(d) Construct an angle of 60° at B and measure BC = 6 cm.

(e) Join C to D and measure the length of CD.

5 (a) Construct triangle PQR where PQ = 11 cm, PR = 9 cm and QR = 6.5 cm.

(b) Construct the perpendicular bisectors of all three sides (they should meet at a point, call it X).

(c) Draw the circumcircle of the triangle – the circle, centre X, passing through P, Q and R.

6 (a) Construct triangle PQR as in Question 5.

(b) Construct the angle bisectors of all three angles (they should all meet at a point, call it Y).

(c) Construct the incircle of the triangle – the circle, centre Y, lying inside the triangle, which just touches each of the sides PQ, PR and QR.

7 (a) Construct an accurate copy of triangle UVW, shown in the diagram.

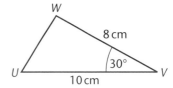

(b) Measure the length of UW.

(c) Construct the perpendicular from W to side UV.

(d) Construct the bisector of angle U.

(e) If these lines meet at point P, measure VP.

Exercise 8iii   **Links: 8G, 8H**

What you should know

A locus is a set of points that obey a given rule.

Always make a sketch of what is required then construct the locus using standard constructions.

1 (a) Construct triangle ABC where AB = 8.5 cm, AC = 5.8 cm and BC = 5 cm.

(b) Shade the region where points are
  (i) nearer to B than A
  (ii) closer to CB than AB.

2 **(a)** Construct triangle *PQR* where *PQ* = 10 cm, *PR* = 8.5 cm and *QR* = 7 cm.

   (b) Shade the region where points are
   (i) more than 6.5 cm from *P*
   (ii) nearer to *R* than *Q*
   (iii) closer to *QR* than *PR*.

3 **(a)** Construct triangle *XYZ* where *XY* = 9 cm, *XZ* = 7.5 cm and angle *YXZ* = 60°.

   (b) Shade the region where points are
   (i) nearer to *Z* than *X*
   (ii) closer to *YZ* than *XZ*
   (iii) less than 6 cm from *Y*
   (iv) less than 5 cm from *Z*.

4 The diagram, which is *not* drawn accurately, shows two cars *A* and *B*.
A is 1200 m north of B.
C is a police car that is checking the speed of cars using its laser detection equipment. *C* is 1600 m east of B.
The equipment can monitor cars up to 800 m away.

Use a scale of 1 cm = 200 m.

A •

B •   • *C*

Make an accurate copy of the positions of *A*, *B* and *C*, then answer these questions.
A travels on a bearing of 110° and *B* travels on a bearing of 075°

   (a) Work out the distance for which each car is within the range of the speed-detector equipment.

   (b) Which car, *A* or *B*, passes closest to the police car, *C*, and by how much?

5 The diagram shows a sketch of a public park, *PQRS*, with distances and angles as shown.

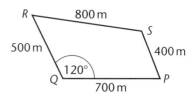

   (a) Draw an accurate diagram of the park using a ruler and compasses only.
   Use a scale of 1 cm = 100 m.

   (b) A statue is to be built at a point, *X*, such that it is
   (i) equidistant from *R* and *S*
   (ii) equidistant from *RS* and *RQ*.
   Mark the position of the statue and find its distance from *P*.

6 The diagram shows a sketch of a quadrilateral *JKLM*, with distances and angles as shown.

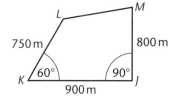

(a) Draw an accurate diagram of the quadrilateral using a ruler and compasses only.
Use a scale of 1 cm = 100 m.

(b) Shade the region that is
   (i) nearer to *J* than *M*
   (ii) closer to *LM* than *LK*
   (iii) within 800 m of *K*.

(c) What is the shortest distance from *M* to any point in this region?

7 The diagram shows a sketch of a triangular area of sea where divers are trying to locate a shipwreck. *D* is due West of *E*.

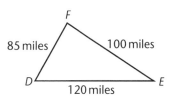

(a) Draw an accurate diagram of the triangle using a ruler and compasses only.

Use a scale of 1 cm = 10 miles.

(b) The shipwreck is known to be
   (i) between bearings of 170° and 200° from *F*
   (ii) nearer to *F* than *D*
   (iii) closer to *DE* than *FE*
   (iv) within 50 miles of *F*.
Shade the region where the shipwreck can be found.

Checklist

You should know how to ...	Grade	For more help, look back at Student Book pages...
construct a triangle given all three sides	E	125–126
construct perpendicular bisectors and angle bisectors	C	126–128
construct the perpendicular to and from a line segment	C	128–129
construct angles of 60°, 90°, 30° and 45°	C	130–132
solve problems involving scale drawing, loci and bearings.	D/C	132–138

Exercise 9i

Links: 9A, 9B

> **What you should know**
>
> Primary data is data you collect yourself. Secondary data comes from existing records (e.g. books or the internet).
>
> When you have a large amount of data, start by organising it in a frequency table or frequency distribution. For continuous data, group the data together in class intervals.

1 State whether each source below is primary or secondary.
 (a) Conducting a whole school survey.
 (b) Information collected using www.bbc.co.uk.
 (c) Television ratings published in a newspaper.
 (d) Using your own specially designed questionnaire.

2 State whether each of the following sets of data are quantitative or qualitative.
 (a) weight (b) country of birth (c) hair colour
 (d) length of cars (e) favourite hobby

Quantitative data contains numbers.
Qualitative data uses descriptive words.

3 State which of the following sets of data are discrete or continuous.
 (a) volume (b) number of cars in a car park
 (c) age (d) building heights (e) shoe size

Discrete data is 'countable'.
Continous data can take any value within a range.

4 A survey of house prices ($\times$ £1000) in a local newspaper is shown below.

172	207	182	225	159	259	160	190
459	465	499	395	169	228	239	199
249	272	210	229	289	239	245	225
204	187	169	252	475	365	455	198
225	245	219	295	235	232	219	315

Construct a grouped frequency diagram showing the tally and frequencies using class intervals 150–199, 200–249....

5 The masses, m, in grams, of 40 tomatoes were recorded as follows.

42	52	51	42	55	47	58	60
49	40	51	52	39	36	52	49
46	50	37	50	58	41	46	50
46	54	48	52	46	48	38	50
54	45	44	38	52	47	46	50

Construct a grouped frequency diagram for this data and include the tally and frequencies using class intervals, beginning with $35 \leqslant m < 40$.

6   The maximum daily temperatures, t (°C), recorded by a weather
station are shown below.

19	19	20	22	24	25	25	24
25	22	20	20	19	17	17	18
21	22	22	19	16	14	15	14
18	20	22	24	25	26	26	

Construct a frequency table using six equal class intervals,
beginning with $14 \leqslant t < 16$.

Exercise 9ii   **Links: 9C**

> ## What you should know
>
> A questionnaire can be used to collect primary data. Ask specific questions and keep the
> questions short and simple.
>
> A sample is part of a whole population. Random sampling gives every member of the
> population an equal chance of being selected. Systematic sampling selects a member of the
> population at regular intervals (e.g. every tenth member from an unordered list). Stratified
> samples take a fair proportion of members from each subgroup within the population.

1   'Food in large supermarkets is cheaper than similar products
bought in local shops.'

   (a) Design a questionnaire to test this hypothesis.

   (b) What method of sampling would you use?

   (c) How will you ensure that your sample is representative?

> A hypothesis is simply a statement that you wish to test.

2   'Older people have smaller, newer cars.'
Describe how you would collect information to test this
hypothesis. Explain how you would select your sample and
give examples of questions in your questionnaire.

> Be aware of the type of questions you can ask in a questionnaire. Always test your questionnaire – a pilot study – on a few people to begin with.

3   'Shorter, but more frequent, school terms would help students
learn.'
How would you find out if this is true or not? What questions
would you ask in your questionnaire? How would you make
sure that your results were unbiased.

> Biased results are ones that are not representative of the population.

4   A headteacher is looking at the amount of homework done by
students. She takes a stratified random sample of 100 students.
The number of students in each year is shown in the table.

Year	7	8	9	10	11
Number of students	235	218	228	205	196

Calculate the number of students from each year group in the sample.

5 A group of students are conducting a survey to establish the population of rock hyraxes in an area around Mount Kenya. In the first week they caught and tagged 34 hyraxes and then released them. In the second week they caught 46 hyraxes, of which 8 hyraxes were tagged. Use these values to estimate the total number of hyraxes in this area.

Exercise 9iii

Links: 9D

What you should know

Two-way tables are similar to frequency tables but show two or more types of information at the same time.

1 The cost of car hire (£) in France can be found in the following table. The minimum hire charge is 2 days.

Car type	Number of days hire						Extra day
	2	**3**	**4**	**5**	**6**	**7**	
Clio	62	92	123	154	184	189	5
Megane	67	101	134	167	201	206	5
Laguna	82	123	164	205	246	253	7
Omega	112	167	223	279	335	342	7
Espace	149	223	298	372	446	456	10

Bus timetables, league tables, school performance tables and holiday brochure prices are all examples of two-way tables.

(a) What is the cost of hiring a Renault Laguna for 4 days?

(b) What is the hire cost for a Vauxhall Omega for 1 day?

(c) Work out the hire cost for an Espace for 15 days.

2 The costs of a river cruise and combined river and aquarium cruises are shown in the table.

	River cruise		Plus aquarium
	Single	**Return**	**Return**
Adult	£2.40	£4.65	£5.50
Child (3–4 years old)	Free	Free	£1.20
Child (5–15 years old)	£1.35	£2.60	£3.40
Concession*	£1.85	£3.40	£4.50
Family (2 adults and 3 children)	£6.65	£11.99	£15.45

* Students and OAPs.

(a) Work out the cost for a return river cruise for three adults and three children (all over 5 years old).

(b) Is this cheaper than buying a family ticket plus one adult ticket? If so, what is the saving?

(c) What is the cost for a return ticket for an OAP and two children (aged 4 and 7 years, respectively) to visit the aquarium on the river cruise?

3 The table shows the repayments schedule for various loans over three different repayment periods. The amounts shown are the monthly repayments with financial protection.

Loan value	3 years	5 years	7 years
£3000	£108	£74	£60
£5000	£180	£123	£100
£10 000	£361	£246	£200
£15 000	£542	£369	£300

(a) What are the monthly repayments for an £8000 loan taken out over 5 years?

(b) How much money in total is repaid on a £20 000 loan taken out over 7 years?

Mixed Exercise

1 For each measure, state whether the data is discrete or continuous.

(a) kg   (b) mm   (c) size 10   (d) 3 acres

(e) 67°   (f) 4 goals   (g) 15″ collar   (h) 2 l

2 The age, a, of each member entering a fitness centre one morning was monitored:

26	28	42	50	22	35	47	39
56	61	64	48	51	27	31	52
59	46	33	27	18	18	39	50
41	25	37	64	44	40		

Using groups $10 \leqslant a < 20$ etc, construct a frequency table showing tally marks and frequencies.

3 Waseem wants to survey students in his school about their reading habits.

(a) Write a question that would help him to investigate how often students read for pleasure. Include a response section.

(b) There are 600 students in Waseem's school. He samples 50 students at random and asks them to complete his survey. He finds that 30 students in the sample read magazines. Estimate the number of students in the school who read magazines.

4 Gareth is carrying out a survey on the use of mobile phones in school. The table shows the number of students in Years 10 and 11.

	Year 10	Year 11
Number of girls	97	93
Number of boys	108	103

Gareth takes a stratified random sample of 50 students from Year 10 and 11. Work out how many girls and boys from each year should be in his sample.

5 Conservation scientists conducted a survey of the Fraser dolphin. In an initial 6-month period, they 'tagged' 128 dolphins. During the next four 6-month periods, they monitored the number of Fraser dolphins that were tagged and the results are shown in the table.

6-month period	Sample size	Number of dolphins 'tagged'
1	96	3
2	152	4
3	143	2
4	77	1

Use this information to estimate the total number of Fraser dolphins in the world.

Checklist

You should know how to...	Grade	For more help, look back at Student Book pages...
identify different types of data	D	143–144
construct frequency tables for discrete and grouped data (using class intervals for grouped data)	D	145–148
create a questionnaire based on a hypothesis	D/C	148–150
use random and representative sampling techniques	A	150–153
design and use two-way tables for discrete and grouped data.	D	153–157

Exercise 10i

Links: 10A–C

What you should know

Bar charts can show patterns or trends in data. The bars can be either vertical or horizontal, but they must be of equal width. Compound bar charts can be used to make comparisons. There are gaps left between the bars for discrete data, but no gaps are left when the data is continuous.

Vertical line graphs can be used to show discrete data. Use a thick vertical line instead of a bar.

For grouped continuous data, draw a frequency diagram with a continuous horizontal scale and no gaps between the bars.

Pie charts show how data is shared or divided. The angle of each sector allows an approximate value to be given to that particular quantity. Always include a key to explain what each sector means.

In a line graph, the points plotted are joined with straight lines. Line graphs show trends in the data. You can only draw line graphs for continuous data.

> Bar charts can be used for quantitative or qualitative data.
>
> Bar charts are also called 'frequency diagrams'.
>
> Line graphs that show how something changes over time are called 'time series'.

1 A box of old mixed nails was being sorted into nails of different lengths (in inches) and the results are shown in the table.

Nail length	Frequency
$\frac{1}{2}''$	18
$1''$	47
$1\frac{1}{2}''$	12
$2''$	21

Draw a vertical line graph for this data.

2 The table shows the results of a survey on the width of pupils' hand-spans, w (in cm).

> Line graphs are similar to bar charts but use a thick line instead of a bar; they are only used for discrete data.

Hand-span (cm)	Frequency
$15 < w \leq 17$	4
$17 < w \leq 19$	6
$19 < w \leq 21$	12
$21 < w \leq 23$	7
$23 < w \leq 25$	3

Draw a frequency diagram to show this information.

3 The number of Sunday newspapers sold in a local shop was recorded as follows.

Newspaper	Number sold
Observer	17
Sunday Times	35
Sunday Telegraph	26
Sunday Mirror	47
News of the World	75

Extend the table to include the sector angle and draw a pie chart to show this information.

4 In a science experiment the current (*I*) in amps was measured through a bulb as the voltage (*V*) was increased.
Here is the table of results.

Voltage (*V*)	2	4	6	8	10	12
Current (*I*)	1.8	2.8	3.5	4.1	4.6	5.0

(a) Plot the line graph to show these results.

(b) What was the approximate value of the current when the voltage through the bulb was 7 *V*?

5 The table below shows the amount of snowfall (in cm) that fell *each hour* during the night.

Time	1100	0000	0100	0200	0300	0400	0500
Snowfall (cm)	1	3	5	6	4	2	1

(a) Plot a graph to show this information. Use the *y*-axis to indicate the amount of snowfall and the *x*-axis for the time.

(b) How much snow fell in total between 11 PM and 5 AM?

Exercise 10ii
Links: 10D, 10E

What you should know

A stem-and-leaf diagram keeps the original data and gives a 'picture' of the spread of data.

Scatter graphs help you to compare two sets of data and to show if there is a connection or correlation between the two quantities. Correlation can be positive or negative, or there could be no correlation.

1   The masses (in grams) of 40 plum tomatoes were recorded as follows.

42 52 51 42 55 47 58 60 49 40
39 36 52 49 46 50 37 50 58 41
46 54 48 52 46 48 38 50 54 45
52 47 46 50 51 52 46 50 44 38

Draw a stem-and-leaf diagram for these results.

2   The results show the width of pupils' hand-spans (in cm).

15.2 15.8 16.0 16.4 17.3 17.4 17.9 18.1 18.3 18.7 19.0
19.2 19.2 19.5 19.9 20.1 20.1 20.4 20.7 20.7 20.8 20.9
21.3 21.5 21.5 21.6 21.7 21.8 22.4 23.0 23.2 24.3

Draw a stem-and-leaf diagram to show these results. Use the key 16|7 to represent 16.7.

3   The table below shows the goal difference and number of points gained for all 20 teams in the Premiership Division mid-way through the season (2005–2006).

Goal difference	28	17	12	9	8	1	7	9	3	1	−5	−5	−3	−4	−10	−14	−8	−13	−12	−20
Points	43	37	31	30	30	28	27	26	25	25	22	21	19	19	17	17	16	13	12	5

(a)   Plot a scatter graph to show these results and draw the line of best-fit.

(b)   What type of correlation do you obtain? Comment on the results.

4   The table shows the fuel consumption for a car journey using the motorways.

Number of kilometres travelled (km)	0	50	100	150	200	250	300
Number of litres left in fuel tank (l)	25.0	20.1	16.7	12.8	8.3	4.4	0.5

(a)   Draw a scatter graph and line of best-fit for this data.

(b)   Comment on the type of correlation found.

Exercise 10iii

What you should know

You can display grouped data in a frequency polygon. Draw a bar chart and then join the mid-point values (middle values) of each class interval using straight lines.

1 A survey of house prices in a local newspaper is shown in the grouped frequency table. Draw a frequency polygon for this data.

House price, p (£000)	Frequency
$150 \leqslant p < 200$	10
$200 \leqslant p < 250$	17
$250 \leqslant p < 300$	5
$300 \leqslant p < 350$	1
$350 \leqslant p < 400$	2
$400 \leqslant p < 450$	0
$450 \leqslant p < 500$	5

2 The maximum daily temperatures, T (°C), recorded by a local weather station during July are shown in the frequency table.

Temperature, T (°C)	Frequency
$14 \leqslant T < 16$	3
$16 \leqslant T < 18$	3
$18 \leqslant T < 20$	6
$20 \leqslant T < 22$	5
$22 \leqslant T < 24$	5
$24 \leqslant T < 26$	7
$26 \leqslant T < 28$	2

Draw a frequency polygon to show the variation in temperature.

Exercise 10iv

Links: 10G

What you should know

Data that is grouped and continuous can be displayed as a histogram. The bars represent the different class intervals and the area of each bar is proportional to its frequency. The vertical axis shows the frequency density.

1 Batteries are tested by putting them into toys and seeing how long they last. Here are the results of 60 tests.

Time , t (min)	Frequency
$500 \leqslant t < 600$	8
$600 \leqslant t < 700$	15
$700 \leqslant t < 750$	10
$750 \leqslant t < 950$	18
$950 \leqslant t < 1150$	9

Draw a histogram to show this information.

2 The histogram below shows the ages of members of a local sports centre. Estimate how many people are members of the sports centre.

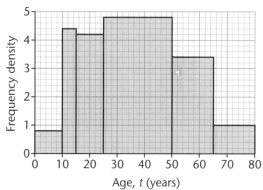

Mixed Exercise

1 The table below shows the temperature of water in a kettle after boiling and then allowed to cool.

Time after boiling (min)	0	2	4	6	8	10
Temperature (°C)	100	50	30	25	22	21

(a) Plot the graph of the results.

(b) What was the water temperature after 3 minutes?

2 The following pie chart shows the areas of four major oceans (in millions of square miles).

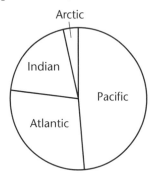

By measuring the angles to the nearest degree, work out the areas of each of the oceans if the total area is 144 million square miles.

3 The maximum and minimum monthly temperatures (°C) in Wellington (New Zealand) are shown for January through to December.

Maximum temperature (°C):
20, 21, 20, 16, 14, 12, 11, 12, 13, 15, 17, 20

Minimum temperature (°C):
13, 14, 12, 10, 8, 6, 5, 7, 8, 9, 10, 11

(a) Copy and complete the stem-and-leaf diagram for the maximum temperature using the key 1|3 to represent 13°C.

(b) Draw a similar stem-and-leaf-diagram to show the minimum temperature.

4 The velocity needed to escape from a planet is given in the table below.

Planet	Diameter (km × 1000)	Escape velocity (km/s)
Mars	4.8	4.3
Venus	12.1	10.4
Earth	12.7	11.2
Mercury	6.8	5.0
Pluto	2.3	1.2

(a) Plot a scatter graph on graph paper to show the relationship between the escape velocity and planet size.

(b) Draw the line of best fit. What type of correlation is obtained?

(c) What can you deduce from this correlation?

5 The frequency table shows the distribution of the mass of 32
Year 8 students (the mass is shown to the nearest kilogram).
Draw a histogram to show this information.

Mass, m (kg)	Frequency
$30 \leqslant m < 34$	2
$34 \leqslant m < 40$	3
$40 \leqslant m < 48$	14
$48 \leqslant m < 60$	7
$60 \leqslant m < 75$	6

Checklist

You should know how to...	Grade	For more help, look back at Student Book pages...
draw bar charts, pie charts, line graphs, stem-and-leaf and frequency diagrams	E to C	160–172
construct scatter diagrams, identify correlation and find the line of best fit	D/C	172–176
construct frequency polygons and histograms.	C to A	176–182

11 Expanding brackets and factorising

Algebra **2**

Exercise 11i

Links: 11A–C

> **What you should know**
>
> To multiply algebraic terms, remember that $x \times 3$ is written as $3x$ and $y \times y = y^2$.
>
> To expand brackets, multiply each term inside the bracket by the term outside the bracket.
>
> To add and subtract expressions with brackets, expand the brackets first and then collect like terms.

1 Simplify these expressions.

(a) $7 \times 3a$ (b) $4f \times 6g$ (c) $4x \times 9x$

2 Simplify the following by multiplying out the brackets.

(a) $4(t + 3)$ (b) $2(c + 7)$ (c) $3(8 + h)$

(d) $5(7 + x)$ (e) $7(f + g)$ (f) $6(a + b + c)$

(g) $3(z - 9)$ (h) $2(r - 8)$ (i) $7(6 - d)$

(j) $4(p + q)$ (k) $5(x + y - 5)$ (l) $8(j - k + l)$

Examples:
$4(a + 3b) = 4a + 12b$
$x(x - 3) = x^2 - 3x$

3 Expand the brackets in these expressions.

(a) $3(2a + 5)$ (b) $2(4b + 1)$ (c) $5(x + 2y)$

(d) $4(3p - 5q + r)$ (e) $3(z^2 + 4z - 1)$ (f) $4(y^2 - 5y - 7)$

(g) $v(v + 3)$ (h) $x(x - 6)$ (i) $n(5n + 2)$

(j) $g(2g - l)$ (k) $-2a(3a + t)$ (l) $3x(5x - 4y)$

(m) $x(x^2 - 5)$ (n) $t(t^2 + 3t)$ (o) $-2p(4p^2 - p)$

Remember
$+\text{ve} \times +\text{ve} = +\text{ve}$
$-\text{ve} \times -\text{ve} = +\text{ve}$
$+\text{ve} \times -\text{ve} = -\text{ve}$
$-\text{ve} \times +\text{ve} = -\text{ve}$

4 Remove the brackets then simplify these expressions.

(a) $2(d + 4) + 3d + 6$ (b) $3(e + 5) + 6e + 1$

(c) $3(p + 5) + 4(p + 1)$ (d) $4(k + 3) + 5(5k + 4)$

(e) $3(3z - 1) + 6(z + 5)$ (f) $5(2t - 3) + 4(3t - 2)$

(g) $4(2j - 1) - 3(j + 7)$ (h) $4(a + 5) - 5(3a + 4)$

(i) $5(r + 5) - 3(r - 4)$ (j) $7(t + 2) - 6(t - 3)$

(k) $3(2x - 1) - 4(x + 4)$ (l) $8(y - 3) - 4(2y - 3)$

Multiply out the brackets and then collect like terms.

Example:
$4(2a + 3) - 2(a - 8)$
$= 8a + 12 - 2a + 16$
$= 6a + 28$

Exercise 11ii

What you should know

To solve equations involving brackets, expand the brackets first.

To solve inequalities involving brackets, expand the brackets and then solve. Rememb_ _ _ _o state all possible values of the solution set.

1 Solve these equations.

(a) $3(t + 2) = 18$

(b) $4(a - 2) = 16$

(c) $5(x - 3) = 45$

(d) $7(p + 7) = 56$

(e) $2(3t + 4) = 38$

(f) $6(4y - 1) = 42$

(g) $3(2b + 5) = 36$

(h) $3(3n + 8) = 6$

2 Solve these equations.

(a) $5(h - 1) = 2h + 4$

(b) $10a + 8 = 4(a + 5)$

(c) $7n + 6 = 3(3n - 2)$

(d) $2(4g + 3) = 9g + 8$

(e) $9(b - 2) = 6(b - 1)$

(f) $5(4x - 3) = 3(2x + 9)$

(g) $3(2t + 3) = 4(2t + 1)$

(h) $4(2p + 6) = 3(6p + 13)$

> Remove the brackets and then collect the terms in the unknown on one side and the terms that are just numbers on the other side.

3 Solve these equations.

(a) $\dfrac{5a - 1}{3} = a + 3$

(b) $x + 5 = \dfrac{3x + 17}{4}$

(c) $\dfrac{3n - 10}{4} = \dfrac{n - 3}{2}$

(d) $\dfrac{t + 2}{3} = \dfrac{5t + 2}{5}$

(e) $\dfrac{3y - 5}{2} + \dfrac{2y + 4}{5} = 4$

(f) $\dfrac{5x + 6}{2} - \dfrac{2x + 3}{6} = \dfrac{x + 2}{3}$

4 Solve these inequalities.

(a) $4(r - 2) < 20$

(b) $2(3d + 2) \geqslant 5$

(c) $2(3z - 4) \leqslant 2 + 7z$

(d) $2(2x + 5) > 3(3x - 2)$

(e) $-1 < 2(y + 3) < 8$

(f) $0 < 3(2t - 9) < 3$

> Remember to include the inequality sign in your answer.

Exercise 11iii

Links: 11G

What you should know

To factorise an expression, look for common factors.

Factorise these expressions.

1 (a) $3k + 15$

(b) $6j + 6$

(c) $8 + 4l$

(d) $5i + 10$

(e) $4p - 16$

(f) $14 - 2q$

(g) $5x - 30$

(h) $18 - 3y$

> *Examples:*
> $5a + 15 = 5(a + 3)$
> $b^2 - 4b = b(b - 4)$
> $9x^2 - 6xy = 3x(3x - 2y)$

2 (a) $r^2 + 3r$ (b) $d^2 - 7d$ (c) $u^2 + u$

Remember, $8t = 2 \times 4t$

    (d) $5s - s^2$ (e) $8t + 6$ (f) $10a - 15$

    (g) $8 - 12h$ (h) $30 - 18x$

3 (a) $9p^2 + 24p$ (b) $3a^2 + ab$

    (c) $8x^2 - 6xy$ (d) $p^3 + 5p^2$

    (e) $p^2q - 8pq + 6pq^2$ (f) $x^3y + x^2y^2 - xy^3$

    (g) $6a^2b + 9a^2 - 3ab^3$

Exercise 11iv

Links: 11H–J

> ## What you should know
>
> To multiply two brackets, multiply each term in one bracket by each term in the other.

Expand and simplify:

1 $(x + 7)(x + 3)$ **2** $(n + 1)(n + 8)$

3 $(k + 5)(k + 6)$ **4** $(y + 4)(y - 1)$

5 $(j - 1)(j + 6)$ **6** $(a - 3)(a - 4)$

7 $(r + 3)(r + 5)$ **8** $(f - 7)(f - 8)$

9 $(p + 4)(p - 9)$ **10** $(g + 4)(6 + g)$

11 $(x + 2)(5 - x)$ **12** $(2 - d)(3 - d)$

13 $(t + 3)^2$ **14** $(z + 2)^2$

15 $(p - 6)^2$ **16** $(x + 7)(x - 7)$

17 $(b + 4)(b - 4)$ **18** $(x + y)(x - y)$

19 $(2x + 3)(x + 4)$ **20** $(3y + 1)(y - 2)$

21 $(2z + 5)(3z + 4)$ **22** $(2p + 5)(2p - 7)$

23 $(q - 5)(3q - 4)$ **24** $(4r - 1)(9 + r)$

25 $(6a - 1)(2 + 3a)$ **26** $(2x + y)(x + 5y)$

27 $(3a - 4b)(2a + b)$ **28** $(3x + 5)^2$

29 $(4y - 3)^2$ **30** $(7 - 2p)^2$

31 $(4k - 3)(4k + 3)$ **32** $(2 - 5w)(2 + 5w)$

33 $(7x + t)(7x - t)$

Examples:

$(x - 4)(x + 6)$
   $= x^2 - 2x - 24$
$(2x + 1)(3x + 2)$
   $= 6x^2 + 7x + 2$

Remember you can use a grid to help.

You are squaring an expression in questions 13–15 and 28–30.

Mixed Exercise

1 Remove the brackets and simplify, if possible.

    (a) $3(8 + d)$ **(b)** $n(5n - 2)$

    (c) $3(4x + 2) - 4(2x + 5)$

2 Solve the following.

    (a) $4(2x - 5) = 5x + 1$ **(b)** $5(2r - 1) \geqslant 32$

    (c) $\dfrac{t + 7}{3} = \dfrac{3t + 1}{4}$

3 Factorise the following.

    (a) $7x - 21$ **(b)** $4a - a^2$

    (c) $9y^2 - 6yz$ **(d)** $x^2y + 10xy - 15xy^2$

4 Expand the brackets:

    (a) $(q + 4)(q + 6)$ **(b)** $(f - 5)(f + 7)$

    (c) $(a + 4)^2$ **(d)** $(3t + 4)(5t - 1)$

    (e) $(4r - 9)(3r - 7)$ **(f)** $(2a + 5)^2$

Checklist

You should know how to...	Grade	For more help, look back at Student Book pages...
expand brackets	D/C	185–189
solve equations and inequalities with brackets	D to B	190–194
factorise by finding common factors	D to B	194–196
expand two brackets.	C to A	196–200

Exercise 12i

Links: 12A

> **What you should know**
>
> A formula shows how quantities or variables are related.

1 Tej buys x lemons, which each cost 24 pence. Tej pays with a £5 note. Write a formula for the change (C), in pence, that Tej should receive.

2 Taxis can take 5 passengers each and minibuses can take 11 passengers each. Write down a formula for the total number of passengers (P) that can be taken by t taxis and m minibuses.

3 A car hire company charges £28 for each days hire plus an extra £35. Write a formula for the charge (c), in pounds, to hire a car from this company for d days.

4 A rectangle has a length of $2x - 1$ and a width of $y + 3$. Write down a formula for the perimeter (P) of the rectangle.

Exercise 12ii

Links: 12B, 12C

> **What you should know**
>
> When substituting numbers into expressions and formulae, remember to follow the correct order of operations.

1 If $a = 5$, $b = 6$ and $c = -3$, find the value of these expressions.

(a) $\dfrac{a + 7}{2}$

(b) $\dfrac{2a + b + c}{2}$

(c) $3a^2 - 8$

(d) $2b^2 + 2c + 5$

(e) $a(b - 1)$

(f) $3(4c + 2)$

(g) $c(3b - 2a - 1)$

(h) $\dfrac{4b + 6}{a}$

(i) $\dfrac{3a + 4c + 2b}{c}$

Brackets
Indices
Multiply/divide
Add/subtract

Remember the division line acts like a bracket

2 Copy and complete these tables.

(a)

x	1	2	3	4	5
$x^2 + 4x$			21		

(b)

x	7	8	7.5	7.3	7.2
$x^3 + 2x$			528		

3 Use the formula $u = \sqrt{v^2 - 2as}$ to calculate u, when
   (a) $v = 10$, $a = 3$ and $s = 6$
   (b) $v = 8.5$, $a = -9.8$ and $s = 10.7$.

4 The formula for the area of a trapezium is $A = \frac{1}{2}(a + b)h$.
   (a) Find the value of A when $a = 9$, $b = 5$ and $h = 3$.   Brackets first.
   (b) Find the value of h when $A = 40$, $a = 6$ and $b = 4$.

Exercise 12iii   Links: 12D, 12E

What you should know

The subject of a formula appears only once, on its own and on one side of the formula.

You can rearrange a formula to make a different variable the subject.

1 Rearrange each of these formulae to make t the subject.
   (a) $r = t + 6$ **(b)** $d = t - 5$
   (c) $h = 4t$ **(d)** $s = pt$

2 Rearrange each of these formulae to make x the subject.
   (a) $y = 3x + 1$ **(b)** $z = 6x - 7$
   (c) $y = 6 - 2x$ **(d)** $p = \frac{1}{2}x - 3$
   (e) $q = \frac{1}{3}x + 5$ **(f)** $u = 4(x + s)$

Remember, always do the same to both sides.

3 Rearrange each of these formulae to make a the subject.
   (a) $b = a^2 - 3$ **(b)** $d = \frac{a^2}{5}$
   (c) $k = \frac{a^2}{2} - 1$ **(d)** $g = \frac{a^2 + 2}{4}$

4 Rearrange each of these formulae to make r the subject.
   (a) $p = \sqrt{r + t}$ **(b)** $w = \sqrt{rs} - 1$
   (c) $V = \pi r^2 h$ **(d)** $4(r + p) = 5p + 1$
   (e) $A = x^2 - \pi r^2$ **(f)** $a = 3 + 2\sqrt{\frac{r}{n}}$

Exercise 12iv

Links: 12F

> ## What you should know
> Trial and improvement is a method to find an approximate solution to an equation.

Use trial and improvement to find the solution, correct to 1 decimal place, to each of these equations.

1 $x^3 + x = 40$

Copy and continue this table to help you:

x	$x^3 + x$	Comment
3	30	Too small
4		

2 $x^3 + 2x = 5$ **3** $x^3 - 4x = 750$ **4** $x^3 + x^2 = 235$

Use a table to help show your method for Questions 2–4.

Mixed Exercise

1 Rachel buys p packs of tomatoes, which each cost 62p. Rachel pays with a £10 note.

Write a formula for the change (C), in pence, that Rachel should receive.

2 Use the formula $s = ut + \frac{1}{2}at^2$ to find the value of s, when
 (a) $u = 5$, $a = 10$ and $t = 4$
 (b) $u = 3.4$, $a = -9.8$ and $t = 2.5$

Give your answer to Question 2(b) correct to 3 s.f.

3 Rearrange each of these formulae to make k the subject.
 (a) $h = k + 3$ (b) $g = 5k - 2$
 (c) $j = \frac{1}{4}k + 2p$ (d) $l = k^2 - n$
 (e) $3(k - d) = 2d + 4f$ (f) $t = \dfrac{3\sqrt{k} + 2}{5b}$
 (g) $s = ut - \frac{1}{2}kt^2$

4 Use trial and improvement to find the solution, correct to 1 decimal place, to the equation $x^3 - x^2 = 54$.

Checklist

You should know how to...	Grade	For more help, look back at Student Book pages...
write a formula	D/C	202–203
substitute into expressions and formulae	D/C	203–206
change the subject of a formula	C/B	208–210
use trial and improvement.	C	211–213

13 Indices

 Exercise 13i Links: 13A–G

What you should know

To multiply powers and roots of the same number or variable, add the indices.

To divide powers of the same number or variable, subtract the indices.

To raise a power to a power, multiply the indices.

Any number or variable raised to the power 1 is equal to the number or variable itself.
Any number or variable raised to the power 0 is equal to 1.

$a^m \times a^n = a^{m+n}$

$b^m \div b^n = b^{m-n}$

$(c^m)^n = c^{m \times n}$

$3^1 = 3 \quad x^1 = x$

$3^0 = 1 \quad x^0 = x$

---

1 Complete the following calculations, giving your answer to 3 significant figures.

(a) $2.7^4 + \sqrt[3]{649}$

(b) $5.8^6 - \sqrt[4]{2473}$

(c) $\dfrac{\sqrt[5]{86273}}{(0.5)^5}$

2 Simplify the following expressions.

(a) $a^4 \times a^3$

(b) $2b^3 \times 3b^6 \times b$

(c) $c^7 \div c^3$

(d) $16d^6 \div 2d^4$

3 Simplify each of the following expressions.

(a) $\dfrac{7^3 \times 7^7}{7^4 \times 7^4}$

(b) $\dfrac{t^3 \times t^4 \times t^2}{t^5 \times t^6}$

(c) $\dfrac{3h^5 \times 4h^3}{2h^2 \times 3h^6}$

4 Simplify each of the these and write your answer
(i) using negative indices   (ii) as a fraction.

A negative index is the same as a reciprocal.
$\dfrac{1}{x^3} = x^{-3}$

(a) $p^2 \div p^4$

(b) $\dfrac{18p^3}{6p^4}$

(c) $\dfrac{1}{p^2} \times \dfrac{1}{p^3}$

(d) $p^{-6} \div p^{-2}$

5 Find the value of your answers to Question 4 when $p = 2$.

6 Simplify the following expressions.

(a) $ab^2 \times a^3b^2$

(b) $6r^2s^{-1} \times 3r^{-4}s^{-3}$

(c) $6a^{-2}b^3 \times \dfrac{4a^4b^5}{2a^5b^{-2}} \times 2b^{-4}$

7 Simplify

(a) $(t^3)^4$ (b) $(2t^2)^3$ (c) 6^0

(d) $(3x)^0$ (e) 7^1.

Exercise 13ii

Links: 13H, 13I

What you should know

Fractional indices are used to express roots of numbers or variables.

In general, $\sqrt[n]{x} = x^{\frac{1}{n}}$ $x^{\frac{m}{n}} = (\sqrt[n]{x})^m$ or $\sqrt[n]{x^m}$

1 Work out the value of the following, using only the positive root.

(a) $36^{\frac{1}{2}}$ (b) $512^{\frac{1}{3}}$ (c) $81^{-\frac{1}{4}}$ (d) $\left(\dfrac{32}{100\,000}\right)^{\frac{1}{5}}$

Examples:
$a^{\frac{1}{4}} = \sqrt[4]{a}$
$b^{\frac{2}{3}} = \sqrt[3]{b^2}$

2 Work out the value of

(a) $16^{\frac{3}{4}}$ (b) $729^{\frac{5}{6}}$ (c) $32^{\frac{8}{5}}$ (d) $3125^{-\frac{3}{5}}$.

3 Find the value of n in each of the following.

(a) $5^n = 625$ (b) $2^n = \dfrac{1}{256}$ (c) $4^{n-1} = 2^8$ (d) $8^{\frac{4}{n}} = 16$

Exercise 13iii

Links: 13J, 13L

What you should know

All numbers can be expressed in standard form, as $a \times 10^n$, where $1 \leq a < 10$ and $n =$ any power.

1 Write in standard form.

(a) 8 300 000 (b) 0.0072 (c) 14×10^8

Example:
$8136 = 8.136 \times 10^3$

2 Write these as decimal numbers.

(a) 7×10^5 (b) 6.2×10^{-3} (c) 6.24×10^1

3 Complete these calculations, giving your answers in standard form.

(a) $(3.7 \times 10^6) + (4.2 \times 10^5)$

(b) $(8.6 \times 10^{-3}) - (3.25 \times 10^{-4})$

4 If $S = 6 \times 10^{-4}$, $T = 3.2 \times 10^6$, $U = 7.3 \times 10^{-9}$ and $V = 4.7 \times 10^7$, find the value of the following, giving your answers in standard form to 4 significant figures.

(a) TV (b) $V \div S$ (c) $S \div U$ (d) UT

5 It takes 2 weeks for the light from a comet to reach Earth. If light travels at 1.86 x 10^5 miles/s, estimate the distance from the comet to Earth. Give your answer in standard form to 3 significant figures.

Mixed Exercise

1 Simplify the following.

(a) $\dfrac{3^4 \times 3^9}{3^2 \times 3^6}$ (b) $\dfrac{3p^{-2} \times 4p^{-4}}{6p^{-3} \times p^{-7}}$ (c) $\dfrac{3a^2b^3 \times 2a^4b^2 \times 2ab^{-4}}{(2a^3)^2}$

2 Give the value of Question 1(a).

3 Work out the following using only the positive root.

(a) $121^{\frac{1}{2}}$ (b) $343^{\frac{2}{3}}$ (c) $\left(\dfrac{16}{243}\right)^{\frac{3}{5}}$

4 Write in standard form.

(a) 62 300 (b) 0.0703 (c) 0.62×10^5

5 If $A = 5.3 \times 10^4$ and $B = 9.2 \times 10^{-2}$, find the value of the following, giving your answers in standard form to 2 significant figures.

(a) $A + B$ (b) $A - B$ (c) AB (d) $B \div A$

Checklist

You should know about...	Grade	For more help, look back at Student Book pages...
calculating powers and roots	C to A	215–218
laws of indices, including powers of 0 and 1	C/B	218–221
negative indices	B	221–224
fractional indices	A/A*	227–229
standard form.	B	230–236

Exercise 14i

Links: 14A

What you should know

You can use the general rule (*n*th term) of a sequence to find any term in a sequence.

1 For each of the following sequences
    (i) write down the first four terms
    (ii) find the difference between consecutive terms
    (iii) write down the 20th term.

  (a) *n*th term: $2n + 5$ (b) *n*th term: $3n - 4$

  (c) *n*th term: $\dfrac{n + 4}{2}$ (d) *n*th term: $10 - 3n$

> To find the 20th term, substitute $n = 20$ into the expression for the *n*th term.

2 The *n*th term of a sequence is $4n + 3$.

  (a) Work out the value of the fourth term.

  (b) Which term has a value of 47?

  (c) Explain why 73 is not a term in this sequence.

3 The *n*th term of a sequence is $n^2 - 2$.

  (a) Write down the first four terms.

  (b) Write down the 12th term.

  (c) Explain why 36 is not a term in this sequence.

4 The *n*th term of a sequence is $\dfrac{n + 1}{n + 3}$.

  (a) Write down the first four terms of the sequence.

  (b) Write down the tenth term.

  (c) Is $\dfrac{21}{25}$ in this sequence? Explain your answer.

Exercise 14ii

Links: 14B

What you should know

To find the *n*th term of a linear sequence, first look at the difference between consecutive terms. The difference gives you the term in *n*.

Find the *n*th term and the 40th term of each of these sequences.

  1 3, 5, 7, 9...   **2** 8, 11, 14, 17...

  3 1, 6, 11, 16...   **4** 9, 13, 17, 21...

5 4, 10, 16, 22...

6 0, 5, 10, 15...

7 12, 13, 14, 15...

8 −5, −2, 1, 4...

9 16, 13, 10, 7...

10 19, 17, 15, 13...

Exercise 14iii

Links: 14C, 14D

> ## What you should know
>
> You can often use patterns to find the rule for a sequence.
>
> To find the nth term of a simple quadratic sequence, look at the second difference.

1 The diagrams show a sequence of rectangles.

 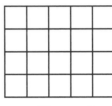

If the second differences are the same, a sequence is quadratic.

Diagram 1
Area = 2 × 3
= 6

Diagram 2
Area = 3 × 4
= 12

Diagram 3
Area = 4 × 5
= 20

(a) (i)   Write down the area of diagram 6.

  (ii)   Write down the area of diagram 15.

  (iii)   Write down an expression for the area of diagram n.

Consider the dimensions of diagram n.

(b) A rectangle in this sequence has an area of 132 cm². What are the dimensions of this rectangle?

2 Find the nth term and the 12th term of each of these sequences.

(a) 2, 5, 8, 17...

(b) −2, 1, 6, 13 ...

(c) 6, 9, 14, 21...

(d) 2, 8, 18, 32 ...

Compare these with the sequence of square numbers.

(e) 10, 40, 90, 160...

(f) $\frac{1}{2}$, 2, $4\frac{1}{2}$, 8 ...

Mixed Exercise

1 The nth term of a sequence is $\dfrac{n + 2}{n + 5}$.

(a) Write down the first four terms of the sequence.

(b) Write down the 15th term.

(c) Is $\frac{29}{31}$ in this sequence? Explain your answer.

2 Find the nth term and the 12th term of each of these
sequences:

(a) 7, 9, 11, 13, ...   (b) 1, 4, 7, 10, ...
(c) −2, 2, 6, 10, ...   (d) 10, 19, 28, 37, ...
(e) −2, −1, 0, 1, ...   (f) 12, 11, 10, 9, ...

3 Find the nth term and the 8th term of each of these
sequences:

(a) 3, 5, 11, 18, ...   (b) 11, 14, 19, 26, ...
(c) −5, −2, 3, 10, ...   (d) 3, 12, 27, 48, ...

Checklist

You should know how to...	Grade	For more help, look back at Student Book pages...
use the general rule/nth term of a sequence	D	238–240
find the nth term of a linear sequence	C	240–241
find the nth term from a sequence of patterns	D/C	241–242
find the nth term of a simple quadratic sequence.	B	243–244

Exercise 15i

Links: **15A**

> **What you should know**
>
> The outcome from an event can be described on a probability scale between 0 and 1.
>
> $$\text{probability} = \frac{\text{number of successful outcomes}}{\text{total number of possible outcomes}}$$
>
> $$\text{relative frequency} = \frac{\text{number of successful trials}}{\text{total number of trials}}$$

1 An octahedral (eight-sided) dice is thrown. What is the probability of the following outcomes?

    (a) throwing a prime number

    (b) obtaining a square number

    (c) obtaining a multiple of 2

    (d) not throwing a 5 or 6

> You can write probability as a fraction, percentage or decimal.

2 In a box there are five dark, six white and seven plain chocolates. What is the probability of picking out one that is

    (a) white   **(b)** dark or plain   **(c)** not plain?

3 A tetrahedral (four-sided) dice is rolled 80 times and the results recorded in the table.

Number	Frequency	Relative frequency
1	16	
2	22	
3		
4	27	
Total		

    (a) Copy and complete the table.

    (b) What are the theoretical probabilities for $P(1)$, $P(2)$, $P(3)$ and $P(4)$?

    (c) How could you make your relative frequencies more accurate?

> $P(1)$ is shorthand for the probability of the outcome being 1.

4 A bag contains 12 green, 8 red and 7 blue counters. A counter is picked at random from the bag. What is the probability that the counter picked will be

    (a) red   **(b)** blue   **(c)** yellow

    (d) not green   **(e)** red, green or blue?

Exercise 15ii

Links: 15B

> ## What you should know
>
> If there are n mutually exclusive outcomes all equally likely, the probability of just one event happening is $\frac{1}{n}$.
>
> If there are n mutually exclusive outcomes and m successful outcomes, the probability of a successful outcome is $\frac{m}{n}$.
>
> For any two outcomes, A and B, that are mutually exclusive and exhaustive:
> $P(A \text{ or } B) = P(A) + P(B) = 1$.
>
> If outcomes A and B are exhaustive, no other outcome is possible.

1 The probability of a school netball team winning their next match is 0.3. The probability of drawing the next match is 0.1. What is the probability that they will

   (a) lose the next match

   (b) win or draw their next match?

2 If one of letter of the word PHILIPPINES is chosen at random, what is the probability of choosing

   (a) I   **(b)** L

   (c) I or P   **(d)** O?

3 A bag contains three red, six blue, five green and six yellow counters. What is the probability of

> The key word to remember here is 'or'.

   (a) picking a blue counter

   (b) not picking a yellow counter

   (c) picking a green or red counter

   (d) not picking a red or blue counter?

4 Balloons are being given out at a party. At the start there are eight red and nine blue balloons.

   (a) What is the probability of being given a red balloon?

   Two blue balloons burst before they can be given out.

   (b) What is the new probability of being given a red balloon?

Exercise 15iii

Links: 15C

What you should know

Always record all the possible outcomes from a single event or two successive events in a systematic way. Use simple lists or sample-space diagrams (two-way tables).

1 An ordinary six-sided dice is thrown together with a 10p coin.
   (a) List all of the possible outcomes systematically.
   (b) Construct and complete a sample space diagram.
   (c) How many outcomes are there altogether?

2 A tetrahedral dice and two coins are tossed simultaneously.
   (a) Construct a sample space diagram to show all the possible outcomes.
   (b) What is the probability of the event (4, head and tail)?
   (c) What is the probability of scoring a 2 with at least one tail?

> Remember, when tossing a coin, HT is different to TH.

Exercise 15iv

Links: 15D

What you should know

Events are independent if they have no effect on each other.

For two independent events, A and B:

$P(A \text{ and } B) = P(A) \times P(B)$.

Total number of outcomes = total number of outcomes from event A
$\times$ total number of outcomes from event B.

1 A coin is tossed three times.
   (a) Draw a tree diagram to show all of the outcomes.
   (b) What is the probability of
       (i) throwing three consecutive heads
       (ii) (head, head, tail)
       (iii) throwing two heads and a tail?

> On a tree diagram, each 'branch' represents one of the possible outcomes.

> You can extend the formula for the total number of outcomes to include three independent events.

2 A four-sided spinner with equal sectors coloured red, green, blue and yellow is used in a game. The spinner is spun twice.
   (a) Draw a tree diagram to represent the probabilities.
   (b) What is the probability of obtaining
       (i) consecutive yellow sections
       (ii) a red–green combination
       (iii) the same colour on consecutive throws?

> The key words to remember here are 'and' or 'all'.

3 A bag holds five red balls and three blue balls. One ball is taken out of the bag at random, its colour noted and replaced. A second ball is then taken out and its colour noted.

  (a) Draw and label a tree diagram to show all the outcomes.

  (b) What is the probability of picking

   (i) two consecutive red balls

   (ii) balls of mixed colour?

Exercise 15v

Links: 15E

> ### What you should know
>
> The probability that one event occurs could depend on another event having taken place. In this case, the second event is conditional.

1 A bag holds five red balls and three blue balls. One ball is taken from the bag and *not* replaced. A second ball is then taken out.

  (a) Draw and label a tree diagram to show all the outcomes.

  (b) What is the probability of picking

   (i) two red balls

   (ii) balls of mixed colour?

  (c) Compare the results with those of Question 3 in Exercise 15iv.

> The key words to remember here are 'without replacement' or 'not replaced'.

2 There are seven blue counters and three red counters in a bag. A counter is picked at random and not replaced. A second counter is then selected. Show that the probability of choosing two counters of the same colour is $\frac{8}{15}$.

3 If it is raining, the probability of Catherine walking to school is 0.1. If it's fine, the probability is 0.8. The weather forecast states that there is a 30% chance of rain tomorrow. Find the probability that Catherine will walk to school.

Mixed Exercise

1 A coloured spinner has numbers 1, 2, 3, 5, 6 and 9.

  (a) Write down the probability that after one spin the number obtained is

   (i) 2

   (ii) even

   (iii) odd

   (iv) 7.

  (b) What is the probability of it landing on a shaded section?

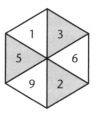

2 A fair six-sided dice is thrown 100 times and the following results are recorded.

Number	1	2	3	4	5	6
Frequency	14	17	12	23	18	16

(a) Write down the relative frequencies for each number.

(b) What is the theoretical probability for each number?

(c) How could the experimental results be improved?

> Sometimes the relative frequency is called the 'experimental probability'.

3 At an outdoor centre, there is a choice of two morning activities (abseiling and sailing) and three afternoon activities (climbing, diving and riding).

(a) Construct a sample space diagram to show all the possible combinations of activities during the day.

(b) As there is an even chance of taking each activity, what is the probability of *not* going climbing?

4 Damien uses the spinner in Question 1. If he spins it twice, what is the probability that the spinner lands on

(a) white twice

(b) shaded, followed by the number 9?

5 There are five red, four blue and three yellow counters in a bag. One counter is picked from the bag, its colour noted and replaced. A second counter is then picked. What is the probability of choosing

(a) two yellow counters

(b) counters of mixed colour?

6 Using the counters from Question 5, one counter is picked at random, its colour noted but is *not* replaced. A second counter is then picked.

(a) Draw a tree diagram to show all the probabilties.

(b) What is the probability of choosing
   (i) two yellow counters
   (ii) counters of mixed colour?

Checklist

You should know how to...	Grade	For more help, look at Student Book pages...
define and use probability and relative frequency	D to B	246–250
deal with mutually exclusive and independent events	D to A	250–252, 253–256
draw and use tree diagrams	C/B	253–257
solve conditional probability problems.	A/A*	256–258

16 Linear graphs

Exercise 16i

Links: 16A

> **What you should know**
>
> A linear graph is the picture of a linear (straight-line) equation.
>
> The highest power of x in a linear equation is 1.

1 Draw these straight-line graphs. For each one

    (i)   make a table of values, choosing at least three values of x

    (ii)   work out the values of y using the equation of the line

    (iii)   plot the points and draw a straight line through them.

    (a) $y = x + 3$ **(b)** $y = x - 4$

    (c) $y = 3 - 2x$ **(d)** $y = 3x + 1$

> In Question 1 **(a)**–**(d)** use the same scale on both axes and draw x- and y-axes between -5 and $+5$.

2 On squared paper draw x- and y-axes from -10 to $+10$. Using x values -6, 0 and $+6$ find the corresponding values for y using the equation $y = \frac{2}{3}x - 3$. Put these results into a table and plot the graph.

> To draw straight line graphs from a linear equation, first construct a table of results for values of x and y, then plot these on a graph.

3 Draw the graph of $y = -5x + 7$ for x values between -1 and $+2$.

4 Draw the graph of $y = 4 - 3x$ for x values between -2 and $+2$.

Exercise 16ii

Links: 16B

> **What you should know**
>
> The coordinates of the mid-point of a line-segment AB, with coordinates $A(x_1, y_1)$, $B(x_2, y_2)$ is given by the equation
>
> $$(x, y) = \left(\frac{x_1 + x_2}{2}, \frac{y_1 + y_2}{2} \right).$$

1 Without drawing these line segments, work out the coordinates of the mid-points.

    (a) $K(6, 4)$ and $L(7, 7)$ **(b)** $M(4, 8)$ and $N(3, 6)$

    (c) $P(5, 6)$ and $Q(-2, -3)$ **(d)** $R(-6, -1)$ and $S(-3, -4)$

Exercise 16iii

Links: 16C

What you should know

For a line that passes through any two points $A(x_1, y_1)$ and $B(x_2, y_2)$ the gradient, m, is given by $m = \dfrac{y_2 - y_1}{x_2 - x_1}$.

The general equation of a straight line is $y = mx + c$, where c is the position the line crosses the y-axis.

Lines that are parallel have the same gradient (same values of m). A line perpendicular (at 90°) to a line with gradient m has a gradient of $-\dfrac{1}{m}$.

1 Find the gradient of the line joining the points

    (a) (1, 5) and (6, 11)   **(b)** (−2, −4) and (3, −5).

> Gradients can be positive or negative.

2 Write down the gradients of the lines that are perpendicular to the lines with the following gradients.

    (a) −4   **(b)** $\frac{3}{2}$ **(c)** 0.6   **(d)** $-2\frac{1}{3}$

Exercise 16iv

Links: 16D

What you should know

The equation of a straight line gives the values of m (the gradient) and c (the y-intercept). Often a linear equation has to be re-arranged into the form $y = mx + c$ before the values of m and c can be obtained.

1 Rewrite the following equations in the form $y = mx + c$. For each one, write down the value of the gradient and intercept.

    (a) $3x + 9 = 3y$ **(b)** $2y - 3x + 2 = 0$

    (c) $-x - y - 1 = 0$ **(d)** $0.2y - 0.3x = 0.6$

    (e) $3x - 4y = 6$ **(f)** $x = -7y + 2$

    (g) $\frac{8}{5} - 2x = 3y$ **(h)** $\frac{1}{12} + \frac{3}{4}x = \frac{5}{3}y$

2 A line has a gradient of −1 and passes through the point with coordinates (3, 5). Find the equation of the line.

3 Find the gradient and equation of the line that passes through the following points.

    (a) (−4, −1) and (4, 7)   **(b)** (−4, 1) and (−3, −2)

4 A line passes through the origin and is perpendicular to the line with equation $y = 4 - 2x$. Find the equation of this line.

Exercise 16v

Links: 16E

> ### What you should know
>
> You can draw the two lines given by two simultaneous equations to find the point at which they cross (the point of intersection). This will give values of x and y that satisfy both equations.

1 Solve these simultaneous equations graphically by following the instructions below.

$$2x - y = 4$$
$$x + y = 5$$

(a) Tabulate the x and y values for x between 0 and 5.

(b) Draw the x-axis between -1 and $+6$ and the y-axis between -5 and $+6$.

(c) Plot the points and find the point of intersection.

2 Find the graphical solution to the following simultaneous equations.

$$3x - 2y = -9$$
$$x + y = 2$$

3 Solve this pair of simultaneous equations graphically.

$$-x - 2y = 2$$
$$5x + 3y = 4$$

Exercise 16vi

Links: 16F

> ### What you should know
>
> Graphs of equations described by inequalities show solutions that are represented by regions.

1 Write down the inequality that describes the shaded regions in the following graphs.

(a)

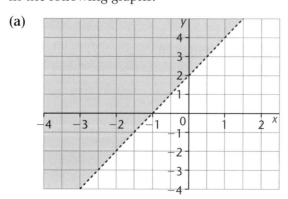

(b)

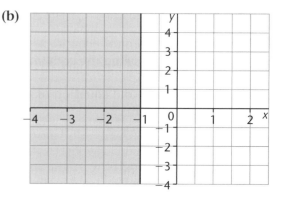

2 Draw a separate graph to show each region that satisfies the following inequalities.

(a) $x + y \geqslant 2$ (b) $y \leqslant 2x$

(c) $y > x + 3$ (d) $x < -4$

> The boundaries of these regions are indicated by a continuous line for $\leqslant$ and $\geqslant$ and a dashed line for $<$ and $>$.

3 On separate graphs, shade in the region that satisfies the following inequalities.

(a) $x > -1$ and $x + y < 2$ (b) $y \leqslant 4$ and $3x + 2y > 1$

4 Sketch the region bounded by the following inequalities and mark it with the letter R.

$$x < 1, \ y \leqslant 4 \text{ and } x + 2y \geqslant 2$$

Exercise 16vii

Links: 16G

What you should know

A conversion graph is used to convert one type of measurement into another, usually with different units. Conversion graphs can be linear or curved.

1 Copy and complete the conversion table between litres and gallons, using the conversion 1 gallon = 4.5 l.

> Only linear conversion graphs are dealt with here.

Gallons (x)	1	2	4	5	8	10
Litres (y)	4.5					45

(a) Draw a conversion graph with an x-axis from 0 to 10 and the y-axis from 0 to 50.

(b) How many litres are there in $7\frac{1}{2}$ gallons?

(c) How many gallons are there in 10 l?

2 Draw a conversion graph between pounds (lbs) and kilograms (kg), using the conversion 1 kg = 2.2 lbs for 0–50 kg.

(a) How many pounds are there in 15 kg?

Exercise 16viii

Links: 16H, 16I

What you should know

Distance–time and velocity–time graphs can be used to work out speed, average speed and acceleration for a particular journey.

$$\text{speed} = \frac{\text{distance}}{\text{time}} \qquad \text{average speed} = \frac{\text{total distance}}{\text{total time}} \qquad \text{acceleration} = \frac{\text{velocity}}{\text{time}}$$

A negative acceleration involves slowing down (or deceleration), usually indicated by a minus sign.

The area under a velocity–time graph gives the distance travelled.

1 This distance–time graph shows the movement of a golf player on the seventh hole of a course.

(a) How long did they take to tee off?

(b) How long did they take to putt on the green?

(c) What was their walking speed after the tee shot?

(d) What was their average walking speed?

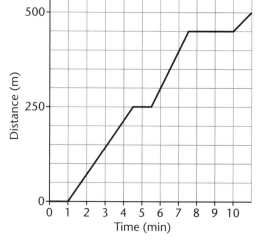

2 The following velocity–time graph shows a short section of a ski run.

(a) Find the total distance travelled.

(b) What was the average velocity for this run?

(c) What was the initial acceleration of the run?

(d) Work out the deceleration before coming to a complete stop.

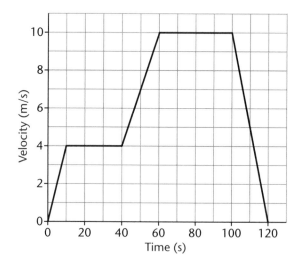

Mixed Exercise

1 Draw the graph of $y = -2x + 5$ for x values between -1 and $+4$

2 Write the equation $5 - 4x = 3y$ in the form $y = mx + c$.

3 (a) Find the equation of the line AB.

(b) Give the y-coordinate of the point on the line with an x-coordinate of 6.

(c) Write down the gradient of a line perpendicular to AB.

(d) Find the coordinates of the mid-point of AB.

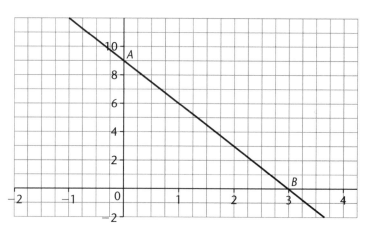

4   Using an x–y grid for x values between -5 and $+4$ and y values between $+10$ and -5, indicate clearly the region defined by the following inequalities. Mark the region with an R.

$$y \leqslant 4, \; x \geqslant -3 \text{ and } y \geqslant x + 2$$

5   Investigate the conversion between grams and ounces using the fact that $1\,oz = 28\,g$.

   (a)   Draw a conversion graph for 0–20 oz.

   (b)   If there are 16 oz in a pound (lb), use your graph to estimate how many grams there are in 1 lb.

6   The velocity–time graph shows part of a train journey between stations.

   (a)   Work out the acceleration after leaving the station (in m/s^2).

   (b)   What was the maximum velocity recorded in metres per second?

   (c)   Find the deceleration of the train as it approached the station (in m/s^2).

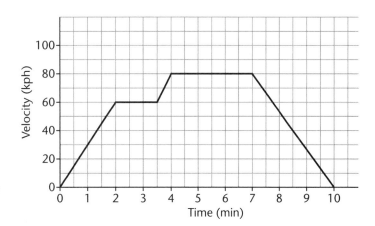

   (d)   Find how far the train travelled between stations in kilometres (to 2 decimal places).

Checklist

You should know how to...	Grade	For more help, look back at Student Book pages...
find the mid-point of a line segment	C	263–264
describe and use the equation $y = mx + c$	B	264–269
find equations of parallel and perpendicular lines through given points	B/A	267–269
solve simultaneous equations graphically	B	272–273
solve graphical inequalities	B	273–276
interpret conversion graphs, distance–time and velocity–time graphs.	D to B	276–282

Exercise 17i

Links: 17A–E

> ### What you should know
>
> A ratio compares two or more quantities.
>
> Ratios can be simplified by dividing by a common factor, or by multiplication. A ratio is in its simplest form when the numbers are integers.
>
> Ratios can be written in the form $1:n$ or $n:1$.
>
> To divide a quantity in a given ratio:
> 1 work out the total number of parts
> 2 work out the value of one part
> 3 work out the value of each share.

1 Feed for horses is made by mixing 5 kg of oats with 3 kg of barley. What mass of oats will I need to mix with 10 kg of barley?

2 Three sprinters complete a race in 14.4 s, 10.8 s and 13.2 s. Write the times as a ratio in its simplest form.

3 (a) Write these ratios in the form $n:1$.
   (i) $17:4$ (ii) $18\,\text{h}:1\,\text{day}$ (iii) $7.65\,\text{kg}:850\,\text{g}$
  (b) Write these ratios in the form $1:n$.
   (i) $9\,\text{mm}:31.5\,\text{cm}$ (ii) $6\,l:750\,\text{m}l$ (iii) $2\,\text{h}\,12\,\text{min}:7.15\,\text{hours}$

4 Share £183 in the ratio $5:4:3$.

5 On Saturday, Jane spends $4\frac{1}{2}$ hours revising maths, geography and french in the ratio of $7:5:3$. How much time does she spend on geography?

Example:
The ratio of nine dogs to six cats can be written as:

$3:2$, $\frac{3}{2}$, $1.5:1$ or $1:0.\dot{6}$.

Example:
Share £21 in the ratio of $5:2$.
$5 + 2 = 7$
£21 ÷ 7 = £3
$5 \times$ £3 = £15
$2 \times$ £3 = £6

Exercise 17ii

Links: 17F–H

> ### What you should know
>
> Two quantities are in direct proportion if their ratio stays the same as they increase or decrease.
>
> Two quantities are in inverse proportion if one increases at the same rate as the other decreases.

1 If 7 kg of beef costs £16.24, how much will 4 kg cost?

2 Tom earns £78.98 for 11 hours' work. He is asked to work 15 hours next week. How much will he earn?

3 I changed £50 into American dollars and received $86. If I change £13.50 into dollars, how many will I get?

4 A refugee camp has enough food for 350 people for 25 days.

   (a) If the food only lasts 14 days, how many people must be in the camp?

   (b) If there are only 225 refugees in the camp, how long will the food last?

▦ Exercise 17iii   Links: 17I–M

> ## What you should know
>
> Ratios are used to describe the scale of a map.
>
> Direct variation is when two quantities increase together.
>
> Inverse variation is when one quantity increases as another quantity decreases.
>
> Always set up an equation using a constant of proportionability.

1 A canal is 54 km long. It is to be shown on a map with a scale of 1 : 400 000. What length will it be on the map?

2 The distance of 72 km is shown as 30 cm on a map. What is the scale of the map?

3 W is proportional to t so that $W = kt$. If $W = 162$ when $t = 18$, find

   (a) the value of k (b) W when $t = 42$ (c) t when $W = 58.5$.

4 In a circuit, the resistance (R ohms) is inversely proportional to the current (C amps). The resistance is 12 ohms when the current is 5 amps.

   (a) Find an equation that connects R and C.

   (b) Find the current when the resistance in the circuit is 20 ohms.

   (c) What would be the resistance in the circuit if the current is 12 amps?

5 Two variables, x and y, vary so that y is directly proportional to the square root of x. When $x = 9$, $y = 21$.

   (a) Find an equation connecting x and y.

   (b) Find y when $x = 12.25$.

   (c) Find x when $y = 40.32$.

6 y is inversely proportional to the cube of x. When $y = 4$, $x = 2$.

   (a) Write an equation connecting x and y.

   (b) Find the value of y when $x = 4$.

Mixed Exercise

1 A drink was made with $1\frac{2}{3}$ cups of apple juice, $\frac{1}{2}$ cup of orange juice and $\frac{1}{4}$ cup of cranberry juice. Write the ratio of apple juice to orange juice to cranberry juice in its lowest terms.

2 A length of wire is cut into three pieces in the ratio of 4 : 5 : 7.

(a) If the shortest piece is 114 cm long, how long is the longest piece?

(b) How long, in metres, was the original piece of wire?

3 If 15 similar cakes have a total mass of 5.4 kg, what is the mass of 7 cakes?

4 If it takes three pumps 16 hours to fill a swimming pool, how many pumps would be needed to fill the pool in 12 hours?

5 The distance from Oxford to York is shown as 38 cm on a map of the UK with a scale of 1 : 750 000. What is the actual distance between Oxford and York in (a) km (b) miles?

7 The speed of a car is inversely proportional to the time the journey takes. When the speed (S) is 60 mph, the time taken (T) is 4 hours.

(a) Find an equation connecting S and T.

(b) Find the time taken when the speed is 50 mph. Give your answer in hours and minutes.

8 Copy and complete the table, where $p \propto q^2$.

> First find the value of the constant of proportionality.

p	126		224
q	6	2.5	

9 Copy and complete the table, where b is inversely proportional to g^3.

b	4.5	−0.288	
g	−2		−3

Checklist

You should know about...	Grade	For more help, look back at Student Book pages...
writing, simplifying and using ratio	E/D	284–289
dividing in a ratio	D/C	289–291
direct and inverse proportion	D/C	291–295
map scales	E/D	296–298
direct and inverse variation.	A/A*	298–307

Exercise 18i

Links: 18A

> ### What you should know
>
> Reflections take place along a mirror line to produce a mirror image. Points on the image are the same distance behind the mirror line as they are on the object in front of the mirror line.
>
> To describe a reflection fully, you need to give the equation of the mirror line.

1 Each diagram shows an object with its image. Copy them onto squared paper and draw in the mirror line in each case.

(a) 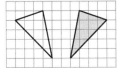   (b)   (c) 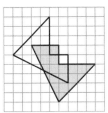   (d)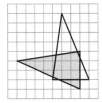

2 Copy these shapes and the dashed mirror line onto squared paper. Draw the reflected image in each case.

(a)   (b)   (c)   (d)

3 Copy the axes and the shape *ABCD* onto squared paper.

  (a) Reflect the shape along the *x*-axis and label the image *A'B'C'D'*.

  (b) What is the equation of this mirror line?

  (c) Now reflect *ABCD* along the line $y = -2$ and label this image *A"B"C"D"*.

  (d) Reflect *ABCD* in the line $y = x$ and label the image *A**B*C*D*.

  (e) What is the connection between the original coordinates of the vertices and the final coordinates?

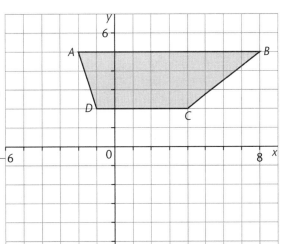

4 Copy the axes and the shape *EFG* onto squared paper.

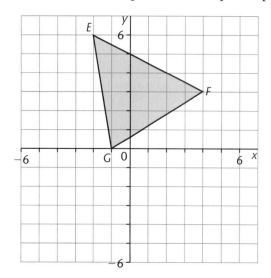

Reflect this shape in the mirror line given by the equation
$x = 1$. Label this image *E'F'G'*. Now reflect this new shape in
the mirror line $y = x$ and label this new image *E"F"G"*.

Exercise 18ii

Links: 18B

What you should know

A rotation turns an object either clockwise or anticlockwise through a given angle about a centre of rotation.

To describe a rotation fully you must give the centre of rotation, the angle of turn and the direction of turn.

1 Copy these shapes onto squared paper. Rotate each shape
about the point *P*

   (i) a one-quarter turn clockwise

   (ii) a one-half turn anticlockwise.

A one-quarter turn is 90°.
A one-half turn is 180°.
A three-quarter turn is 270°.

(a) 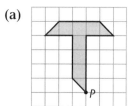   **(b)** 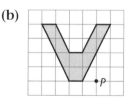   **(c)** 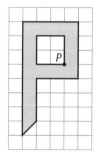   **(d)**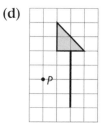

2 Copy this shape onto squared paper and draw the image after it has been rotated about the point *P*

(a) 180° clockwise

(b) 270° anticlockwise

(c) a one-quarter turn anticlockwise.

3 On squared paper, draw both *x*-axis and *y*-axis from −6 to +6. Copy the shape *G* onto your axes.

Draw the image after it has been rotated

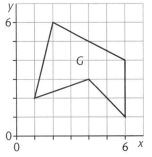

(a) through 90° clockwise about the origin (0, 0). Label this image *G′*

(b) a one-half turn anticlockwise about the point (−2, 1). Label this image *G″*.

4 Describe fully the transformation that maps the shape *H* onto the shape *I*.

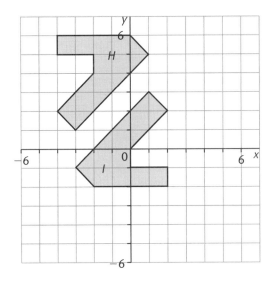

Exercise 18iii   Links: 18C

What you should know

A translation slides a shape from one position to another.

To describe a translation, you need to give the distance and the direction of the movement and this is achieved using a column vector $\begin{pmatrix} x \\ y \end{pmatrix}$.

1 Copy these shapes onto squared paper and translate each one of them by the amounts shown.

(a)   **(b)**   **(c)**

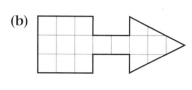

(i) $\begin{pmatrix} 2 \\ 3 \end{pmatrix}$ (i) $\begin{pmatrix} -2 \\ 1 \end{pmatrix}$ (iii) $\begin{pmatrix} -4 \\ -3 \end{pmatrix}$.

In a translation, every point on the shape moves the same distance in the same direction.

2 Copy this shape onto squared paper.

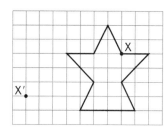

The top number represents the movement in the x-axis direction and the bottom number represents the movement in the y-axis direction.

A translation of the shape moves the point X to the point X' on the image.

(a) Draw the complete image.

(b) What is the column vector that describes the translation?

3 The shape P is translated to new positions Q, R, S, T and U. Describe each translation by giving the column vector.

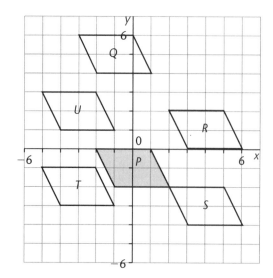

Exercise 18iv

Links: 18D

> ## What you should know
>
> An enlargement changes the size of an object but not its shape. The number of times the shape is enlarged is called the 'scale factor' or 'multiplier'. This can be a whole number or a fraction.
>
> In an enlargement all the angles stay the same but all the lengths are changed in the same proportion. The image is similar to the object.
>
> A negative scale factor produces an image that is in the opposite direction to that of the object.

1 For each of the following shapes, work out the scale factor of the enlargement. The object shape is shown shaded.

(a)    (b) 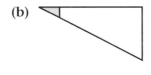   (c)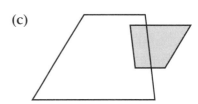

2 Copy each of the following shapes onto squared paper. Enlarge each shape by the scale factor shown in brackets.

(a)
(4)

(b)
(3)

(c)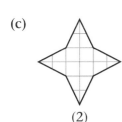
(2)

(d)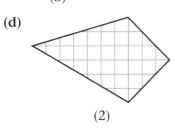
(2)

3 Copy the following shapes onto squared paper. Enlarge each one by a scale factor of 2 from the centre of enlargement at C.

(a) 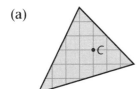   (b)    (c)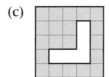

4 The object X is enlarged to produce the image Y. Copy the shapes onto squared paper.

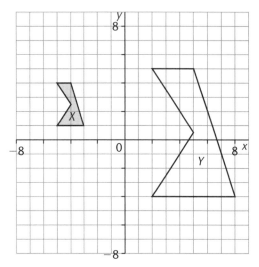

(a) What is the scale factor of the enlargement?

(b) Construct lines to show the position of the centre of enlargement.

(c) What are the coordinates of the centre of enlargement?

Exercise 18v

Links: 18E

> ### What you should know
>
> Combined transformations produce more than one image and can also be described by a single transformation.

1 A triangle ABC has coordinates $A(-9, -4)$, $B(-4, -4)$ and $C(-5, -8)$. It is reflected in the mirror line $y = 1$ and is then reflected again in the line $y = 4$.

> Reflections in parallel lines can be replaced by a single translation.

(a) Draw the image $A''B''C''$ and give the coordinates of the point C''.

(b) Describe the single transformation that takes A to A''.

> Reflections in lines that aren't parallel can be replaced by a single rotation.

2 (a) Draw the x-axis with x values between -13 and $+6$ and and the y-axis with y values between -5 and $+5$.

(b) Draw the triangle ABC with $A(-13, -1)$, $B(-8, 1)$ and $C(-9, -4)$.

(c) Reflect ABC in the mirror line $x = -5$ and label this $A'B'C'$.

(d) Reflect $A'B'C'$ in the line $y = x$ and label this new image $A''B''C''$.

(e) What are the coordinates of A''?

(f) Describe a single transformation that takes A to A''.

Mixed Exercise

1 Copy these shapes on to squared paper and reflect each shape in the mirror line shown.

(a)   **(b)**   **(c)**

2 Rotate the shape T 90° anticlockwise about the point P and label this T'.

Now reflect this new shape in the mirror line $x = 1$ and label this new shape T''.

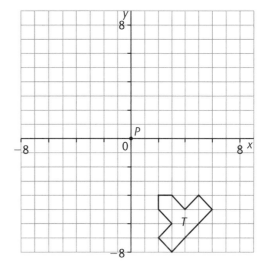

3 Copy the shape Q onto squared paper and translate it through the vector $\begin{pmatrix} -4 \\ -6 \end{pmatrix}$ and label this new shape Q'.

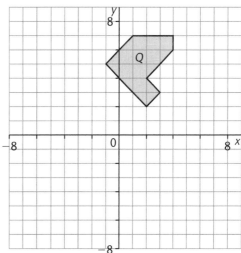

4 Copy the following shape onto squared paper and enlarge it by a scale factor of 2 about the point P.

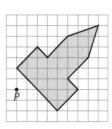

5 Copy the shape S onto squared paper and draw an enlargement with a scale factor of $-\frac{1}{2}$ about the origin. Leave on your construction lines and label the image S'.

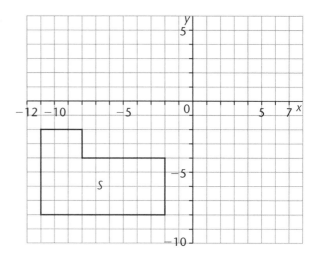

6 Copy the triangle ABC onto squared paper, with both x-axis and y-axis between -9 and $+9$.

  (a) Reflect ABC in the line $y = x$ and label the image $A'B'C'$.

  (b) Reflect $A'B'C'$ in the line $y = -x$ and label the new image $A''B''C''$.

  (c) What single transformation takes ABC directly to $A''B''C''$?

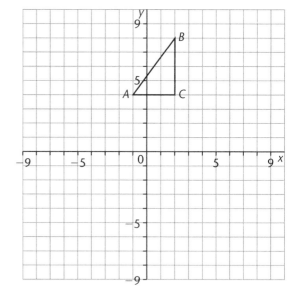

Checklist

You should know how to...	Grade	For more help, look back at Student Book pages...
recognise and use the four types of transformation: refelction, rotation, translation and enlargement	D/C	309–330
enlarge shapes with fractional and negative scale factors	C to A	325–330
find the centre and scale factor of an enlargement	C to A	323–330
use a combination of transformations.	C to A	331–334

19 Congruency and similarity

Shape 5

Exercise 19i

Links: 19A

> **What you should know**
>
> Congruent shapes are identical. All lengths and angles in the object and image are equal.
>
> Similar shapes have the same shape but not the same size. All angles in the object and image are equal but all lengths are only in the same ratio or proportion.
>
> There are four conditions for congruency in triangles:
> SSS – side, side and side
> SAS – side, angle and side
> ASA – angle, side and angle, SAA – side, angle, angle
> RHS – right-angled, hypotenuse and side.

1 Look at the shapes in the diagram.

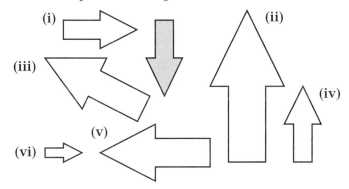

  (a) Write down the shapes that are similar to the shaded one.

  (b) Write down the shapes that are congruent to the shaded one.

  (c) Write down any shapes that are neither similar nor congruent to the shaded shape.

2 Copy these shapes onto squared paper. For each shape, draw an image that is

  (i) congruent   (ii) similar.

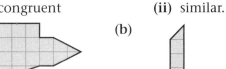 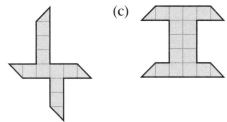

Write down the scale factor for each similar shape you have drawn.

3 For each pair of triangles shown below, give the appropriate reasons for congruency.

(a)

(b)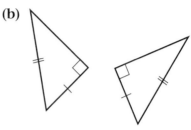

(c)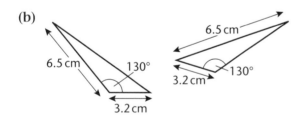

(d)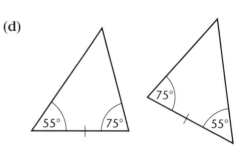

4 Look at the pairs of triangles shown below.
For each pair, say whether they are congruent or not.
Give an appropriate reason if they are congruent.

(a)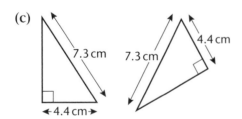

(b)

(c)

(d)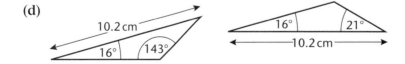

Exercise 19ii

Links: 19B

> **What you should know**
>
> In similar shapes, all lengths are in the same ratio or proportion according to the scale factor (k) of the enlargement.

1 In the following triangle, find the length of

    (a) *DE*   **(b)** *FG*.

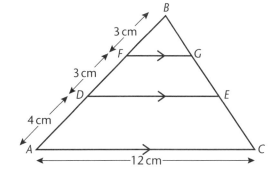

2 A slide projector produces an image 100 cm high from a slide with a height of 2 cm. If the distance from the bulb to the screen is 350 cm, how far away is the slide from the bulb?

> It is important to obtain the correct scale factor by identifying in which direction you are going. When going from a small image to a large image, the scale factor is k. Moving from a large image to a small image has a scale factor $\frac{1}{k}$.

3 A small conifer tree that is 2.5 m tall casts a shadow that is 1.2 m long. How tall is a similar tree that casts a shadow 3.8 m long? Give your answer to 1 decimal place.

4 The diagram shows two similar triangles *ABC* and *BDC*. *BC* = 7 cm and *DC* = 5 cm.

    Calculate the value of *AD*, marked x on the diagram.

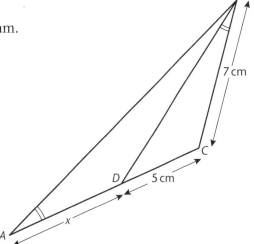

5 The Moon has a diameter of 3476 km. In an experiment it can be covered exactly by a 1p coin placed 221 cm away from the eye. Use the fact that the diameter of a 1p coin is 2 cm to calculate the distance to the Moon.

Exercise 19iii

Links: 19C

> **What you should know**
>
> If a shape is enlarged by a linear scale factor k, then
>
> enlarged area $= k^2 \times$ original area
> enlarged volume $= k^3 \times$ original volume,
>
> where k^2 is the area scale factor and k^3 is the volume scale factor.

1 For the following scale factors, state

(i) the area factor   **(ii)** the volume factor.

(a) $k = 4$ **(b)** $k = 20$ **(c)** $k = 1.6$ **(d)** $k = 0.8$

2 A model kit has a scale factor of 1 : 12. Write down the ratio for

(a) the area factor   **(b)** the volume factor.

3 The area of a kitchen table is 2.8 m². Calculate the area of a similar dining room table that is twice as large.

4 A photo measuring 6 inches by 4 inches is being enlarged by a scale factor of 1.8.

(a) What is the area factor?

(b) Work out the area of the enlarged photo to 2 significant figures.

5 A box is in the shape of a cuboid measuring 2 cm $\times$ 3 cm $\times$ 5 cm. The box is enlarged by a scale factor of 3.

(a) Calculate the surface area of the enlarged shape.

(b) What is the volume of the enlarged box?

6 A glass jug 14 cm tall holds 40 cl of juice. A similar glass jug holds 1.8 l of juice.

(a) What is the volume factor?

(b) How tall is the larger glass jug (to the nearest centimetre)?

Mixed Exercise

1 Are the following pairs of triangles congruent? If so, give the appropriate reason(s).

(a)

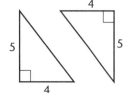

(b)

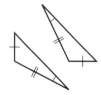

2 The two triangles below are similar with equal angles, as shown. Find the unknown lengths a and b.

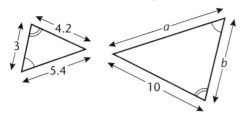

3 A sheet of A4 paper measures 29.56 cm by 20.9 cm. This sheet is then cut in half to give two sheets of A5. Show that both single sheets of A4 and A5 paper are mathematically similar.

4 An oil slick has been measured to cover an area of 20 km^2. Several hours later the length of the slick has doubled. If the basic shape of the slick does not alter, work out the area of the enlarged slick.

5 The height of the great pyramid at Giza, Egypt, is 146 m. The beautifiul pyramid at Saqqara is similar, but its height is only 52.5 m. What are the ratios of the volumes between the two pyramids? Give your answer in the form $1 : x$, where x is given to 3 significant figures.

Checklist

You should know how to...	Grade	For more help, look back at Student Book pages...
define congruency in triangles using the four definitions of SSS, SAS, ASA/SAA and RHS	C	337–340
define similarity and use scale factors	B	340–344
work out areas and volumes of similar figures using scale factors.	A/A*	344–347

Exercise 20i

Links: 20A

> ### What you should know
>
> The three averages are the mean, median and mode. The mode is the value that occurs most often, the median is the middle value when arranged in order of size and the mean is the sum of all the values divided by the number of values, n.
>
> $$\text{Mean } \bar{x} = \frac{x_1 + x_2 + \dots + x_n}{n} = \frac{\sum x}{n}.$$
>
> The symbol $\sum$ means 'the sum of'.
>
> The range is found by subtracting the smallest value from the largest value.

1 Find the mean, mode, median and range for these data sets.

  (a) 3 9 7 8 1 1 7 6 5 5 3 1 4 2

  (b) 100   101   105   99   97   104   101   100   98

  (c) 27   36   41   29   32   28   40   37   35   30   39   41

  (d) 523   516   576   542   533   527   588   544   516   528

2 Find the mean, mode, median and range for these data sets.

  (a) 16.8   17.1   16.5   17.4   16.6   18.1   17.7   16.9   17.3

  (b) 0.6   0.7   0.5   0.5   0.6   0.8   1.1   0.4   0.7   0.4   0.5

  (c) 122.1   120.3   140.7   133.8   139.7   136.4   138.9
       127.6   131.2   125.2   134.4   129.3

  (d) 5.62   5.74   5.83   5.76   5.68   5.81   5.73   5.79   5.62   5.74

3 In a hockey tournament, the number of goals scored in each match were recorded as follows.

  2, 1, 0, 0, 3, 5, 0, 1, 2, 4, 0, 1, 2, 3, 2, 2

  Find the mean, mode, median and range for the number of goals scored.

4 The mass of ten apples were recorded to be 100 g, 104 g, 112 g, 92 g, 96 g, 97 g, 105 g, 110 g, 105 g and 90 g.

  Find the mean, mode, median and range of the mass of the apples.

5 The mass (in tonnes) of eight lorries entering a waste disposal site were measured as follows.

  22.6, 28.1, 20.5, 23.4, 24.7, 19.8, 21.8, 25.1

  Find the mean, mode, median and range of the mass of the lorries.

6 The speed of cars on a local road was measured with a speed gun and the following results were recorded in a stem-and-leaf diagram.

```
2 7 7 8 9
3 0 0 1 1 2 2 2 3 3 3 3 4 4 4 5 7 7 8 8 9
4 0 1 4 7 7 8
5 2 6                        3|4 means 34 mph.
```

(a) Find the mean, mode, median and range of the speeds.

(b) What is the probable speed limit for this road?

Exercise 20ii   Links: 20B

What you should know

You must be able to select an appropriate average to use and give your reasons.

1 In a snooker tournament, the highest breaks recorded by one particular player were 36, 27, 68, 51, 120, 46, 9, 40, 22, 37 and 19.

(a) What is the mean break score?

(b) Is this a sensible average to use for this player? Justify your answer.

2 In a 400 m race the following times were recorded (in seconds):

76, 68, 82, 60, 72, 69, 65, 75, 76, 81, 117, 63

(a) Find the mean, mode and median times for this race.

(b) What would be the most sensible average to use? Justify your response.

(c) What would be the mean value if the extreme time of 117 s was omitted? Comment on your results.

Exercise 20iii   Links: 20C

What you should know

For a large amount of data, you can place the results into a frequency table. The mean value is then given by $\bar{x} = \dfrac{\sum fx}{\sum f}$, where $\sum f$ is the total frequency and $\sum fx$ is the sum of $f \times x$.

The median value depends on the number of data values, n.

If n is an odd number, the median is the $\frac{1}{2}(n + 1)$th value in the ordered list.

If n is an even number, there will be two middle values in the ordered list and the median is the mean of these two values.

1 The number of mobile phone calls made daily were recorded during a 4-week period as follows.

5	6	7	7	6	11	10	6	5	6
8	9	9	12	8	9	5	7	5	8
11	9	5	11	6	6	12	5		

(a) Copy and complete the frequency table below.

Number of calls (x)	Tally	Frequency (f)	fx
5	ЖⅠ	6	30
6			
7			
8			
9			
10	Ⅰ	1	10
11			
12			
		$\sum f = 28$	$\sum fx =$

x is the data and f is the frequency.

(b) Find the mean, mode, median and range for these data.

2 In morse code, letters and the numbers 0–9 are represented by a series of dots and dashes. The number of dots and dashes used can be seen in the following table.

Dots (x)	Frequency (f)	fx	Dashes (x)	Frequency (f)	fx
0	4		0	5	
1	11		1	12	
2	10		2	10	
3	7		3	6	
4	3		4	2	
5	1		5	1	
	$\sum f =$	$\sum fx =$		$\sum f =$	$\sum f =$

(a) Copy and complete the table to include the fx values.

(b) Find the mean, mode and median for both the dots and the dashes.

(c) Comment on your results.

3 A hockey team secretary recorded the number of goals scored during the 2005–2006 season, as shown in the table.

Number of goals (x)	0	1	2	3	4	5
Frequency (f)	6	4	7	1	2	1

(a) Copy and extend the table to include the values of fx.

(b) Work out the values of $\sum f$ and $\sum fx$.

(c) From these values, calculate the mean, median and mode of the number of goals scored in the season.

Exercise 20iv

Links: 20D

What you should know

For large amounts of data, it is easiest to group the data in a grouped frequency table. The groups are called 'class intervals' and the middle values are called the 'mid-interval' values. The mid-interval value is the mean of the two class limits. Only an estimated mean, modal and median value can be obtained because individual data is lost.

The mean value is then given by $x = \dfrac{\sum fx}{\sum f}$,

where $\sum f$ is the total frequency and $\sum fx$ is the sum of $f \times x$.

The x values here are given by the mid-interval values.

1 A breakdown service support vehicle records the number of incidents they attend during a 2-week period.

Number of visits	Frequency (f)	Mid-interval value (x)	fx
3–4	7	3.5	24.5
5–6	20		
7–8	36		
9–10	5	9.5	
11–12	2		23
	$\sum f =$		$\sum fx =$

(a) Copy and complete the table. Use the information to estimate the mean number of visits.

(b) What are the modal and median class intervals for the number of visits?

2 The heights of 32 randomly selected members of the sixth form were recorded as follows.

Height, h (cm)	Frequency (f)	Mid-interval value (x)	fx
$140 \leqslant h < 150$	2		
$150 \leqslant h < 160$	3		
$160 \leqslant h < 170$	6		
$170 \leqslant h < 180$	9		
$180 \leqslant h < 190$	9		
$190 \leqslant h < 200$	2		
$200 \leqslant h < 210$	1		
	$\sum f =$		$\sum fx =$

> Continuous data that is grouped can also be displayed as a histogram. This was covered in Chapter 10.

(a) Copy and complete the grouped frequency table. Use the table to estimate the mean height of the group.

(b) What are the modal and median height class intervals?

3 In a design and technology storeroom the lengths of wood off-cuts were measured and the following results recorded.

Length, l (cm)	Frequency (f)
$20 \leqslant l < 30$	13
$30 \leqslant l < 40$	12
$40 \leqslant l < 50$	19
$50 \leqslant l < 60$	10
$60 \leqslant l < 70$	2

(a) Extend the table to include the mid-interval values for the length (call this x) and the values of fx. Include the values of $\sum f$ and $\sum fx$.

(b) Estimate the mean length of off-cuts in the storeroom.

(c) What are the modal and median class intervals for the lengths of off-cuts in the storeroom?

4 The histogram shows the tests results of the lifespan of some batteries.

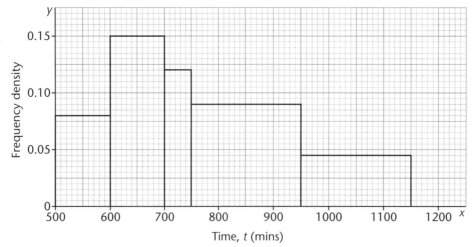

(a) Use the information in the histogram to copy and complete the following table.

Time, t (min)	Frequency (f)	Mid-interval value (x)	fx
$500 \leq t < 600$	9	550	4950
$600 \leq t < 700$			
$700 \leq t < 750$			
$750 \leq t < 950$			
$950 \leq t < 1150$			
	$\sum f =$		$\sum fx =$

(b) Estimate the mean lifespan of a battery (to 3 significant figures).

Exercise 20v

Links: 20E

What you should know

A time-series shows how a particular value changes across time. They are useful when looking for patterns in the data.

Moving averages are used to smooth out either seasonal variations or data containing extreme values to look at long-term trends.

1 The table shows the daily audience figures for a play at the local opera house over a three-week period.

	M	T	W	T	F	S
Week 1	309	268	298	311	415	658
Week 2	278	314	334	299	437	597
Week 3	258	286	275	316	529	712

(a) Plot a graph as a time-series.
(b) Calculate the mean audience for each week.
(c) Work out the 6-day (point) moving averages and plot these on a graph.
(d) Comment on the results.

2 The table shows the percentage of men in Britain who smoked between 1974 and 1988.

Year	1974	1976	1978	1980	1982	1984	1986	1988
%	50	46	45	42	38	36	35	33

   (a) Calculate the 3-point moving average.

   (b) Copy and complete the graph below of this moving average by including your results.

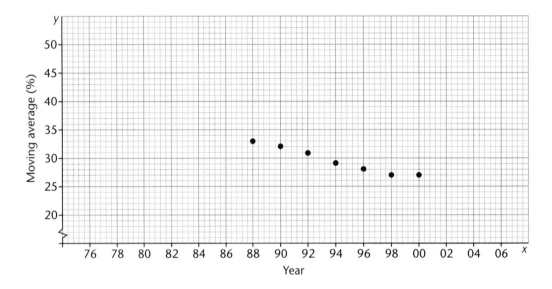

   (c) The government set a target of reducing the percentage of male smokers below 25% by the year 2006. Comment on how probable this target was. Justify your answer.

3 The table shows the number of monthly mobile calls made from a household landline during 2006.

110	86	48	59	78	100	92	56	65	83	137	149
J	F	M	A	M	J	J	A	S	O	N	D

   (a) Plot the results as a time-series.

   (b) Comment on these results.

   (c) Calculate the 4-point moving average and plot these points on the same graph.

   (d) Comment on the trend.

Mixed Exercise

1 Find the mean, mode, median and range for these data sets.
   (a) 36, 10, 24, 0, 56, 20, 6, 12, 10, 18
   (b) 7.2, 6.7, 8.3, 7.7, 8.1, 8.0, 5.9, 6.2, 7.7
   (c) 0.05, 0.03, 0.07, 0.06, 0.06, 0.07, 0.08, 0.05, 0.06

2 The population of the various districts in Cheshire in mid-2003
   were as follows.
       119 100, 91 500, 112 700, 81 000, 150 300, 124 100
   Work out the mean, median and range for these data.

3 The salaries of the work force in a small company were as follows.
   £20 500, £18 700, £15 200, £16 300, £22 800, £39 950, £19 800,
   £18 700
   (a) Find the mean, mode, median and range of the salaries.
   (b) Which average describes the salaries most sensibly?
   (c) What is the mean value when the director's salary of £39 950 is
        not included?

4 The list shows the number of goals scored by a school football team
   in their last 22 matches.
   2 0 1 5 0 3 0 7 2 4 3 0 2 2 0 1 4 6 2 0 1 3
   (a) Construct a frequency table for this set of data.
   (b) From the table work out $\sum f$ and $\sum fx$.
   (c) Calculate the mean, mode and median number of goals scored.

5 In an experiment, the voltage of used AA batteries was recorded and
   the results are shown below.

Voltage, v (volts)	Frequency (f)
$0.0 < v \leqslant 0.3$	2
$0.3 < v \leqslant 0.6$	7
$0.6 < v \leqslant 0.9$	5
$0.9 < v \leqslant 1.2$	13
$1.2 < v \leqslant 1.5$	9

   (a) Copy and extend the table to include the mid-interval values
        (call this x) and the values of fx.
   (b) Work out the values of $\sum f$ and $\sum fx$.
   (c) Estimate the mean voltage of the used batteries.
   (d) What is the voltage value for a new AA battery?

6 The table below shows the winning scores of the British Open Golf Championship between 1978 and 1988.

Year	78	79	80	81	82	83	84	85	86	87	88
Score	281	283	271	276	284	275	276	282	280	279	273

(a) Plot the time-series graph to show these results.

(b) Calculate the 4-point (year) moving average and plot these results on a separate graph.

(c) Comment on any variation shown in the moving averages.

Checklist

You should know how to...	Grade	For more help, look back at Student Book pages...
find the mean, median and mode for discrete data	D/C	350–353
find the range and understand what is meant by the spread of data	D	350
find the mean, median and mode from frequency distributions and grouped frequency distributions for both discrete and continuous data	C	355–362
understand time-series graphs and find moving averages.	B/A	362–365

Exercise 21i

Links : 21A

> **What you should know**
>
> A cumulative frequency table is obtained from a grouped frequency distribution by calculating the running total of the frequency up to the end of each class interval.
>
> Cumulative frequency graphs can be drawn for both discrete and continuous data sets. They are useful for comparing data sets.
>
> The shape of a cumulative frequency diagram (often an 's' shape) reflects the characteristics of the data and how it is spread or distributed within the range.

1 The number of students' absences in a school during a monthly period are shown in the frequency table.

Number of days absent	Frequency	Number of days absent	Cumulative frequency
0–1	64	$\leqslant 1$	
2–3	45	$\leqslant 3$	
4–5	18	$\leqslant 5$	
6–7	6	$\leqslant 7$	
8–9	1	$\leqslant 9$	
10+	2	$\leqslant 30$	

The class intervals are changed to show values 'up to and including' i.e. the upper class boundary.

(a) Copy and complete the cumulative frequency table.

(b) Plot the results in a cumulative frequency graph.

(c) Estimate how many students were absent for more than 4 days.

The 'cumulative frequency' is always plotted on the vertical (y) axis.

2 The frequency table shows the height of 100 students.

(a) Extend the table to include the cumulative frequency.

(b) Plot a cumulative frequency curve.

(c) Estimate the number of students whose height is 168 cm or more.

Height, h (cm)	Frequency
$150 \leqslant h < 155$	13
$155 \leqslant h < 160$	32
$160 \leqslant h < 165$	30
$165 \leqslant h < 170$	15
$170 \leqslant h < 175$	7
$175 \leqslant h < 180$	3

3 The table shows the amount of monthly radiation from the Sun (in kcal/cm^2) falling on the UK.

Month	J	F	M	A	M	J	J	A	S	O	N	D
Radiation	3.1	6.2	11.7	17.3	21.4	23.4	21.9	17.9	12.9	7.8	4.0	2.4

(a) Extend the table to include the cumulative frequency (round the values to the nearest whole number).

(b) Plot the cumulative frequency curve to show this data.

(c) Estimate the amount of radiation falling in the first six-and-a-half months.

4 The cumulative frequency curve for 32 student's hand spans (in cm) is shown below.

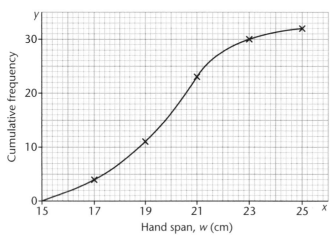

Construct a cumulative frequency table and use this to estimate the number of students whose hand-spans are more than 23 cm wide.

Exercise 21ii

Links: 21B

What you should know

From a cumulative frequency graph, the following statistical measures can be obtained:

median/middle value, $\frac{1}{2}$-way up the axis (50%)

lower quartile (LQ), $\frac{1}{4}$ of the way up the axis (25%)

upper quartile (UQ), $\frac{3}{4}$ of the way up the axis (75%)

interquartile range (IQR) = UQ − LQ.

1 Use the cumulative frequency curve you drew for Question 1 of Exercise 21i to find an estimate for the following.

(a) the median   **(b)** the lower quartile

(c) the upper quartile   **(d)** the interquartile range.

2 The frequency distribution for the mass (in grams) of 40 plum tomatoes is shown below.

Mass, m (g)	Frequency
$35 \leqslant m < 40$	5
$40 \leqslant m < 45$	5
$45 \leqslant m < 50$	12
$50 \leqslant m < 55$	14
$55 \leqslant m < 60$	3
$60 \leqslant m < 65$	1

Draw a cumulative frequency curve and use it to find an estimate for the following.

(a) the median   **(b)** the lower quartile

(c) the upper quartile   **(d)** the interquartile range

Exercise 21iii   Links: 21C

What you should know

A box plot or box-and-whisker diagram, shows the key statistics from a cumulative frequency curve. It should contain the following information.

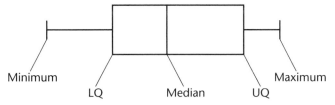

If possible, draw box plots directly under the cumulative frequency graph. If not, you must put a scale underneath the diagram.

1 Using the cumulative fequency curve you drew for Question 2 of Exercise 21ii, draw a box plot for this data. What is the range?

2 The masses (in kg) of 200 students were recorded and the following statistical information was obtained.

minimum = 36, maximum = 75,
median = 54.5, LQ = 49 and UQ = 61.

Draw a box plot for this data. What is the range and IQR?

3 The distances recorded in a long-jump competition are given in order below (all distances given to the nearest centimetre).

112, 146, 152, 168, 183, 226, 235, 276, 288, 294, 308, 311, 312, 325, 333

Draw a box plot for this data. What is the range?

4 The percentage test marks for 96 students sitting a history exam can be summarised in the following way.

minimum = 11, maximum = 96, LQ = 51, UQ = 72 and median = 64.

  (a) Draw a box plot for this data.

  (b) Comment on the results.

5. The box plot shows the results for the heights of 16 girls in a class.

Using the scale below the box plot, estimate

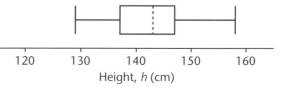

  (a) the median   **(b)** the LQ

  (c) the UQ   **(d)** the minimum

  (e) the maximum.

Exercise 21iv

Links: 21D

What you should know

Cumulative frequency diagrams and box plots are useful when comparing two (or more) sets of data. The spread of data is important in order not to draw false conclusions.

1 These two box plots show the results of tests on the life expentency of two types of light bulbs.

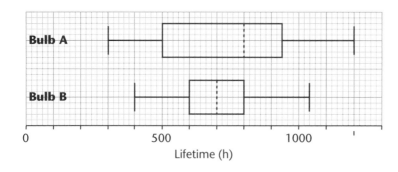

Which bulb is more reliable? Justify your answer.

2 The heights of 50 boys and 50 girls are shown in the
following frequency table.

Height, h (cm)	Frequency (boys)	Frequency (girls)	Cumulative frequency (boys)	Cumulative frequency (girls)
$155 \leqslant h < 160$	2	5		
$160 \leqslant h < 165$	6	9		
$165 \leqslant h < 170$	14	22		
$170 \leqslant h < 175$	19	11		
$175 \leqslant h < 180$	8	3		
$180 \leqslant h < 185$	1	0		

(a) Copy and complete the cumulative frequency table.

(b) For both distributions, construct
   (i) cumulative frequency diagrams
   (ii) box plots.

You can draw two or more
cumulative frequency curves
on the same set of axes.

(c) Estimate the median height for boys and girls and
comment on the results.

3 The masses of 100 parsnips of variety A (gem whites) are
shown in the frequency table.

Mass, m (g)	Frequency
$110 \leqslant m < 115$	9
$115 \leqslant m < 120$	25
$120 \leqslant m < 125$	36
$125 \leqslant m < 130$	19
$130 \leqslant m < 135$	8
$135 \leqslant m < 140$	3

(a) Draw a cumulative frequency diagram with a box plot
below it to represent this distribution.

Another sample of parsnips (variety B – Gladiators) produced
the following statistical information.

minimum = 105 g, maximum = 148 g, median = 124 g,
LQ = 113 g, UQ = 130 g and number in the sample = 74.

(b) Draw a box plot for variety B.

(c) Make three meaningful comparisons between the two
varieties of parsnips.

4 The amount of rainfall (in millimetres) falling each month in two areas of the Indian Himalayas are shown the table.

Month	J	F	M	A	M	J	J	A	S	O	N	D
Darjeeling	10	20	35	100	210	585	800	640	430	130	25	15
Gangtok	20	55	105	245	415	470	575	510	435	115	45	10

(a) Draw a cumulative frequency diagram to show both distributions.

(b) Under the cumulative frequency diagram show a box plot to represent each region.

(c) Compare the distributions and comment on your results. Justify your answers.

Mixed Exercise

1 In a 400 m race the following times were recorded (in seconds).

60, 63, 65, 68, 69, 72, 75, 76, 76, 81, 82

(a) Draw a box plot to represent this distribution.

(b) State clearly the minimum, maximum, LQ, UQ and median values.

2 The table shows the distribution of areas of the major countries in Africa.

Area, A (million km^2)	Frequency
$0 \leqslant A < 0.5$	25
$0.5 \leqslant A < 1.0$	8
$1.0 \leqslant A < 1.5$	8
$1.5 \leqslant A < 2.0$	1
$2.0 \leqslant A < 2.5$	1
$2.5 \leqslant A < 3.0$	1

(a) Extend the table to include the cumulative frequencies.

(b) Draw a cumulative frequency diagram for these data.

(c) Draw a box plot underneath the diagram.

(d) Comment on the distribution.

4   The table below shows the length of words found in a recent
    survey of 100 words in editions of broadsheet and tabloid
    newspapers.

Word length	Frequency (broadsheet)	Frequency (tabloid)	Cumulative frequency (broadsheet)	Cumulative frequency (tabloid)
1	8	9		
2	14	15		
3	25	25		
4	14	17		
5	8	13		
6	7	10		
7	15	8		
8+	9	3		

(a) Copy and complete the cumulative frequency table.

(b) Draw a cumulative frequency diagram to show both sets
     of data.

(c) Draw box plots for both distributions.

(d) Comment on your findings.

Checklist

You should know how to ...	Grade	For more help, look back at Student Book pages...
construct cumulative frequency graphs	B	369–370
find quartiles and interquartile ranges	B	374–376
draw box plots	B	377–379
compare and interpret distributions.	B	380–382

Exercise 22i

Links: 22A

What you should know

Pythagoras' theorem states that in a right-angled triangle, the square of the hypotenuse (the longest side of a triangle) is equal to the sum of the squares on the other two sides.

For a right-angled triangle with side lengths a, b and c, where c is the hypotenuse,

$$a^2 + b^2 = c^2$$

or $\quad a^2 = c^2 - b^2$

or $\quad b^2 = c^2 - a^2$

The hypotenuse is always opposite the right angle.

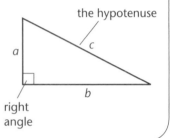

1 Calculate the lengths marked with letters in each of the following triangles.

(a)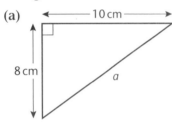

(b)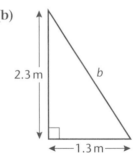

(c)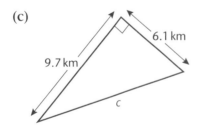

2 A door measures 2.2 m high by 0.8 m wide. Work out the length of the diagonal.

3 A ladder is placed against a vertical wall with its foot 1.2 m away from the wall. If the top of the ladder is 3.4 m above the ground, how long is the ladder?

4 Calculate the lengths **(a)** *AB* **(b)** *EF*.
Give your answers correct to 1 d.p.

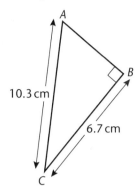 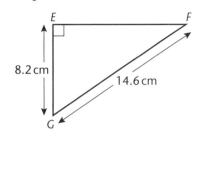

5 Find the altitude of an equilateral triangle of side 8 cm.

6 *ABCD* is a right-angled trapezium with *AB* = 6.7 cm,
DC = 11.6 cm and *AD* = 7.6 cm.

Work out the length of

(a) *BC* **(b)** *AC*.

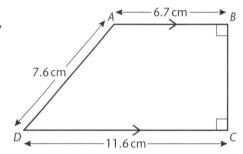

Exercise 22ii

Links: 22B

What you should know

For points $A(x_1, y_1)$ and $B(x_2, y_2)$ the length of *AB* is given by

$$AB = \sqrt{(x_1 - x_2)^2 + (y_1 - y_2)^2}$$

The expression will also work for negative coordinate values.

1 Two points on an *x*–*y* graph have coordinates *P*(5, 7) and
Q(9, 14). Find the length of *PQ*.

2 The top right-hand corner of a square, labelled *A* has
coordinates (2, 3). If the side length of the square is 6 units
find **(a)** the coordinates of the corners *B*, *C* and *D* (clockwise)
       (b) the length *DB* using Pythagoras' theorem.

3 Find the lengths (to 1 d.p.) between the following points that
have coordinates

(a) *R*(−2, 4), *S*(−6, −9)   **(b)** *T*(14, −7), *U*(−7, 15)

(c) *V*(−1, 0), *W*(−2, −1)   **(d)** *X*(−2, −4), *Y*(4, 2)

Exercise 22iii

Links: 22C, 22D

What you should know

Trigonometry involves three ratios called sine, cosine and tangent (or sin, cos and tan).
They are defined for a right-angled triangle as follows.

$$\sin x = \frac{\text{opposite}}{\text{hypotenuse}} = \frac{O}{H}$$

A useful memory aid is
SOHCAHTOA.

$$\cos x = \frac{\text{adjacent}}{\text{hypotenuse}} = \frac{A}{H}$$

$$\tan x = \frac{\text{opposite}}{\text{adjacent}} = \frac{O}{A}$$

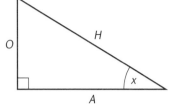

If the lengths of two sides are given you can use trigonometry to work out an angle. To do
this you will need to take the inverse of the function using your calculator.

Inverse functions are usually labelled $\sin^{-1}$, $\cos^{-1}$, $\tan^{-1}$.

1   For the triangle shown, write down the three trigonometric
    ratios for

    (a) angle x

    (b) angle y.

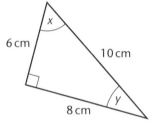

2   Work out the value of the following trigonometric functions
    giving your answer to 4 d.p.

    (a) $\sin 60°$

    (b) $\tan 23°$

    (c) $\cos 45°$

    (d) $\cos 89°$

    (e) $\sin 120°$

    (f) $\sin 150°$

3   Find the value of each angle correct to the nearest degree.

    (a) $\sin y = 0.3907$

    (b) $\cos x = 0.2249$

    (c) $\cos \theta = -0.8192$

    (d) $\tan \phi = 2.6051$

4 Work out the size of the unknown angles (to the nearest degree) in the following triangles. All lengths are in cm.

(a)

(b)

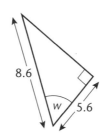

(c)

(d)

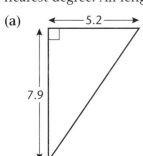

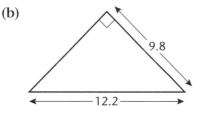

5 Find all the missing angles in these triangles correct to the nearest degree. All lengths are in cm.

(a)

(b)

(c)

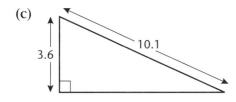

Exercise 22iv

Links: 22E

What you should know

If the length of one side and the size of one angle are given you can use trigonometry to work out the remaining side.

The information given will direct you to the correct trigonometric function to be used.

1 In triangle *ABC*, length *AB* = 6 cm, angle *ACB* = 90° and angle *BAC* = 38°. Work out the lengths of **(a)** *BC* **(b)** *AC*.

2 Calculate the unknown lengths marked on each diagram
(all lengths are in cm) to 1 d.p.

(a)   **(b)** 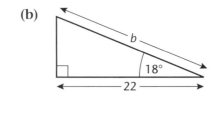   **(c)**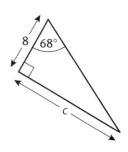

3 In the triangle shown, state which expressions are true (T) or
false (F).

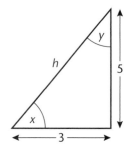

(a) $h = \dfrac{5}{\sin x}$ **(b)** $h = \dfrac{\cos y}{5}$ **(c)** $h = \dfrac{3}{\tan x}$

(d) $h = \dfrac{3}{\sin y}$ **(e)** $h = \sqrt{3^2 + 5^2}$

Exercise 22v   **Links: 22F**

1 In the following diagram find the length marked x.

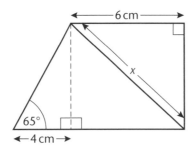

2 *ABCD* is a parallelogram. *AB* = 11 cm and *AE* meets *DC* at 90°.
Using the information given, find the length of the longest
diagonal *DB*.

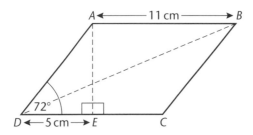

3 A circle of radius 4 units is centred on the origin of an *x*–*y* coordinate grid as shown below.

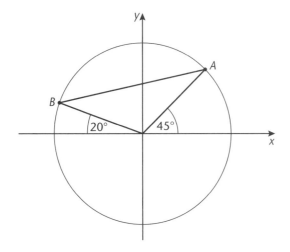

(a) Find the coordinates of the points *A* and *B*.

(b) Find the length of *AB*.

Exercise 22vi

Links: 22G, 22H

> ## What you should know
>
> Pythagoras' theorem and trigonometry can be used to solve problems.

1 A yacht sails from a harbour, *H*, for 8 km due north to a point *A*. It then changes direction and sails 12 km on a bearing of 090° to point *B*. Find

(a) the distance *HB* to 1 d.p.

(b) the angle *HBA* (to the nearest degree).

2 A wooden platform rests horizontally on the third rung of a set of stairs as shown in the diagram.

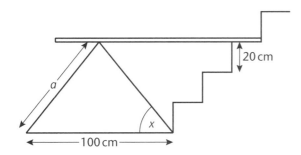

Each stair step rises 20 cm. An isosceles triangle framework supports and maintains the ladder in this position. Calculate
(a) the base angle *x* and (b) the side length, *a*, of the support.

Exercise 22vii

Links: 22I

What you should know

The angle of elevation is the angle measured upward from the horizontal.

The angle of depression is the angle measured downward from the horizontal.

1 A hot air balloon is at an altitude of 350 m. Its landing site is located at a horizontal distance of 2 km from the balloon. What is the angle of depression?

2 Another balloon is seen 3400 m away from the first balloon but flying at an altitude of 520 m. What is the angle of elevation between the balloons?

Exercise 22viii

Links: 22J

What you should know

Pythagoras' theorem and trigonometry can also be used to solve problems in three dimensions (3-D). First identify and draw the correct right-angled triangle that contains the length or angle to be found.

The length, x, of the longest diagonal in a cuboid with dimensions a, b and c is given by

$$x^2 = a^2 + b^2 + c^2$$

You can also use trigonometry and Pythagoras' theorem to find the angle between a line and a plane.

1 A cuboid has side lengths $a = 4$ cm, $b = 5$ cm and $c = 11$ cm. Work out the length of the longest diagonal of the cuboid. (Give your answer to 1 d.p.)

2 *ABCDEF* is a equilateral triangular prism as shown in the diagram below. $FC = 6$ cm and $DC = 14$ cm. The line *EM* meets the line *AD* at right angles. Calculate

   (a) the height *EM*

   (b) the length *EC*

   (c) the angle *ABM*

   (d) the angle between *ED* and the plane *ABCD*.

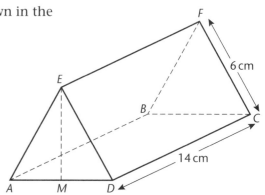

Mixed Exercise

1 A piece of A4 paper 20.9 cm wide by 29.4 cm long is folded in half to form a sheet of A5 paper. Work out the length of the diagonals of **(a)** the A4 sheet **(b)** the A5 sheet.

2 Two points have coordinates $(-2, -7)$ and $(3, 9)$. Calculate the distance between the points.

 3 Using your calculator, work out the following functions giving your answer to 4 d.p.

    (a) $\tan 127°$ **(b)** $\cos 6°$ **(c)** $\cos 121°$

 4 Use your calculator to find the value of each angle to the nearest degree.

    (a) $\tan A = 28.6363$ **(b)** $\sin B = 0.9976$

5 The Great Pyramid at Giza in Egypt is a square-based pyramid with the dimensions shown in the diagram.
Calculate

    (a) the length AC

    (b) the angle between EA and the base $ABCD$.

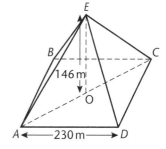

Checklist

You should know how to...		For more help, look back at Student Book pages...
apply Pythagoras' theorem to right-angled triangles	C to A	385–389
find the distance between two coordinate points	B	389–390
use the basic trigonometric functions, sine, cosine and tangent	B	390–401
solve problems in three dimensions.	A/A*	401–405

Exercise 23i

Links: 23A

What you should know

The perpendicular from the centre of a circle to a chord bisects
the chord.

Tangents drawn to a circle from an external point are
equal in length.

The angle between a tangent and a radius is 90°.

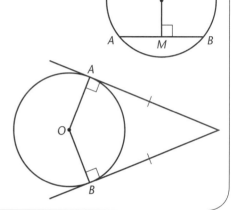

Find the angles labelled with letters or the sides indicated in each
of the following.

1

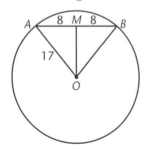

Find *OM*.

2

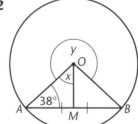

3

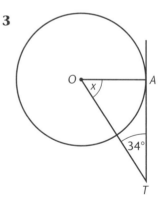

4

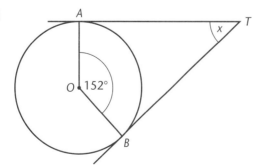

5

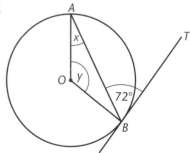

6

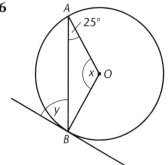

7

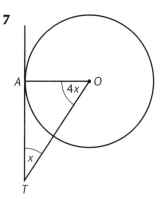

8

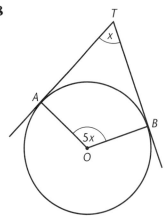

Exercise 23ii

Links: 23B

What you should know

The angle subtended by an arc at the centre of a circle is twice the angle that it subtends at the circumference.

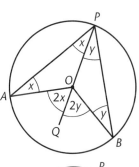

The angle in a semi-circle is a right angle.

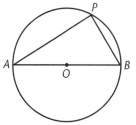

Find the angles labelled with letters in each of the following.

1

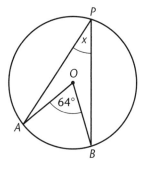

2

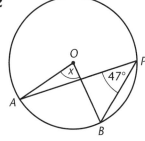

3

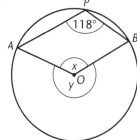

4

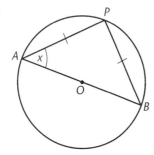

5

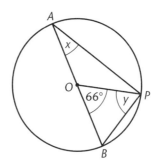

6

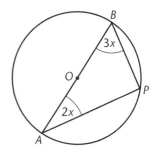

7

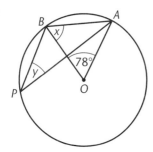

8

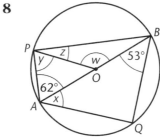

9

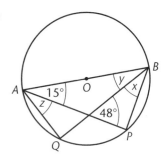

Exercise 23iii

Links: 23C

> ### What you should know
>
> Angles in the same segment are equal.
>
>   angle APB = angle AQB
>
>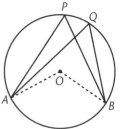
>
> Opposite angles of a cyclic quadrilateral are supplementary.
>
> angle ABC + angle ADC = 180°
>
> An exterior angle of a cyclic quadrilateral is equal to the opposite interior angle.
>
> angle ABC = angle CDE
>
>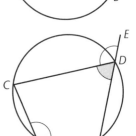

Find the angles labelled with letters in each of the following.

1

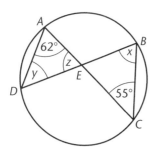

2

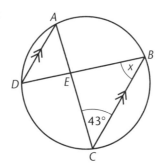

3

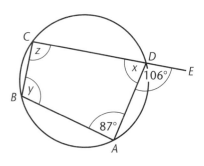

4

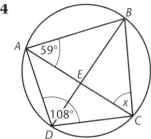

5

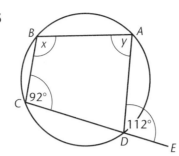

6

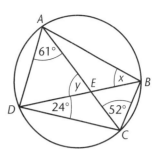

7

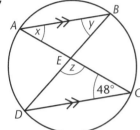

8

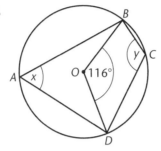

9

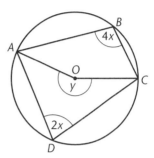

Exercise 23iv

Links: 23D

Find the angles labelled with letters in each of the following.

1

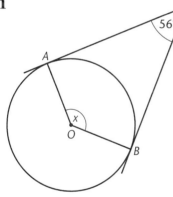

2

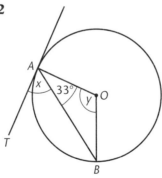

3

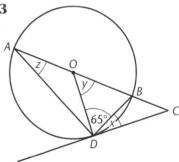

4

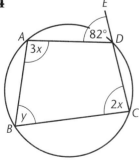

5

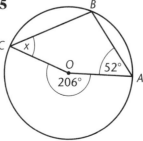

6

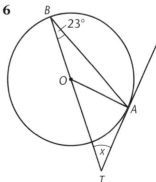

7

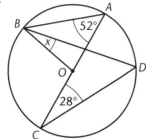

8

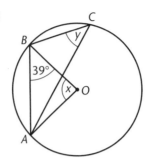

9

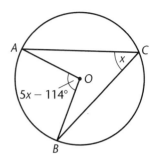

Exercise 23v

Links: 23E

What you should know

The angle between a tangent and a chord is equal to the angle in the alternate segment.

angle TAB = angle APB

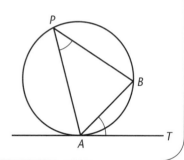

Find the angles labelled with letters in each of the following.

1

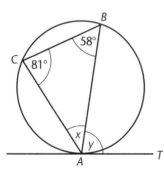

2

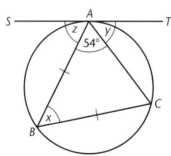

3

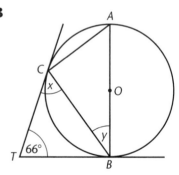

4

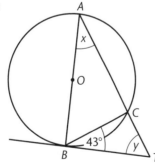

5

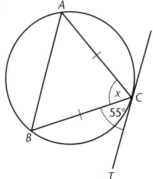

6

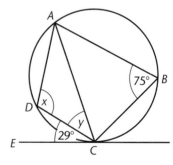

7

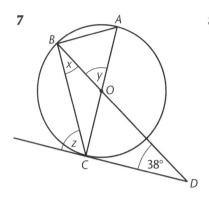

8

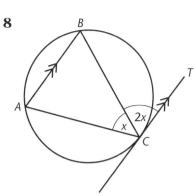

9

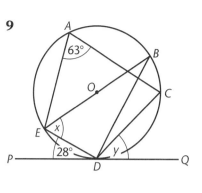

Mixed Exercise

Find the angles labelled with letters in each of the following.

1

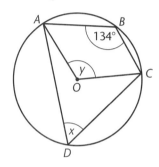

2

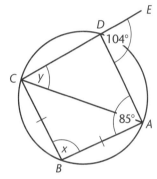

3

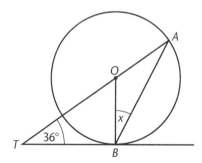

4

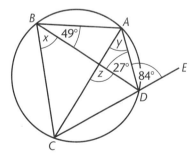

5

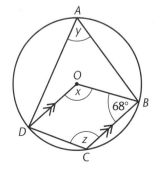

6

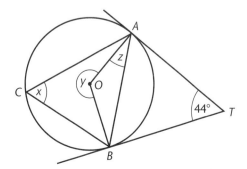

7

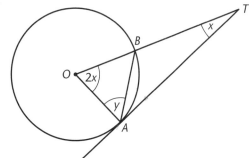

8

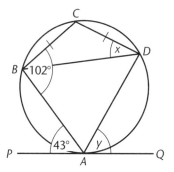

9

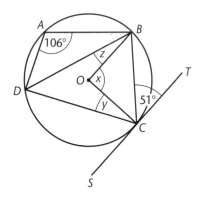

Checklist

You should know how to ...	Grade	For more help, look back at Student Book pages...
circle properties	B	408–410
circle theorems	B	411–421
the alternate segment theorem.	A	421–423

Exercise 24i

Links: 24A

What you should know

$$(x + a)(x - a) = x^2 - a^2$$

The difference of two squares means that any expression of the form $x^2 - a^2$ can be factorised into two factors that differ only in that the sign in one bracket is $+$ and in the other is $-$.

1 Factorise

(a) $x^2 - 81$

(b) $y^2 - 49$

(c) $w^2 - 144$

(d) $p^2 - q^2$

(e) $m^2 - n^2$

(f) $4x^2 - 25$

(g) $64a^2 - 9$

(h) $100 - 81y^2$

(i) $121 - 16m^2$

(j) $9t^2 - 25w^2$

(k) $20b^2 - 245n^2$

(l) $48x^2 - 3y^2$

Exercise 24ii

Links: 24B

What you should know

A quadratic expression of the form $x^2 + bx + c$ will often factorise into two brackets.

1 Factorise

(a) $a^2 + 11a + 10$

(b) $b^2 + 5b + 4$

(c) $c^2 + 8c + 12$

(d) $d^2 + 16d + 39$

(e) $x^2 + 8x - 9$

(f) $y^2 + 4y - 32$

(g) $w^2 + w - 30$

(h) $t^2 + 12t - 28$

(i) $m^2 - 5m - 6$

(j) $n^2 - 2n - 15$

(k) $p^2 - 3p - 18$

(l) $q^2 - 13q - 48$

(m) $a^2 - 8a + 16$

(n) $b^2 - 12b + 20$

(o) $x^2 - 15x + 36$

(p) $y^2 - 13y + 42$

Exercise 24iii

Links: 24C

What you should know

When factorising quadratics of the form $ax^2 + bx + c$ you first have to consider the factors of the coefficient of x^2.

1 Factorise

(a) $2x^2 + 15x + 7$

(b) $2y^2 + 11y + 12$

(c) $3a^2 - 17a + 10$

(d) $5m^2 + 31m + 6$

(e) $2w^2 - w - 15$

(f) $3t^2 + 2t - 8$

(g) $5n^2 + 33n - 14$

(h) $7p^2 - 29p + 4$

(i) $4x^2 + 16x + 15$

(j) $6y^2 + y - 12$

(k) $4w^2 - 27w + 18$

(l) $6t^2 + 59t - 10$

(m) $9b^2 - 42b + 48$

(n) $40x^2 + 76x - 60$

Exercise 24iv

Links: 24D

What you should know

Some quadratic equations can be solved by rearranging the terms.

1 Solve
- **(a)** $2x^2 = 32$
- **(b)** $3y^2 - 147 = 0$
- **(c)** $9x^2 - 1 = 0$
- **(d)** $(y - 4)^2 = 49$
- **(e)** $(w + 5)^2 = 121$
- **(f)** $2(t - 3)^2 = 128$
- **(g)** $3(y - 10)^2 - 243 = 0$
- **(h)** $5(x + 2)^2 - 180 = 0$

2 Solve these equations, giving your answers correct to 3 s.f.
- **(a)** $(x + 3)^2 = 5$
- **(b)** $(y - 4)^2 = 11$
- **(c)** $2(w - 5)^2 = 14$

Exercise 24v

Links: 24E, 24F

What you should know

Some quadratic equations can be solved by factorising.

Rearrange the equation so that all the terms are on one side and are equated to zero.

Then factorise the quadratic expression.

Solve these quadratic equations.

1 (a) $x^2 - 4x = 0$ **(b)** $w^2 + 8w = 0$ **(c)** $4a^2 - 10a = 0$

2 (a) $b^2 - 8b + 7 = 0$ **(b)** $x^2 - 4x - 12 = 0$ **(c)** $y^2 + 5y - 14 = 0$

3 (a) $x^2 = x + 6$ **(b)** $w^2 = -11w - 28$ **(c)** $64 = 16a - a^2$

4 (a) $5t^2 + t = 0$ **(b)** $3x^2 - x = 0$ **(c)** $2y^2 + 5y = 0$

5 (a) $2x^2 - 3x - 2 = 0$ **(b)** $5m^2 - 18m - 8 = 0$ **(c)** $3t^2 - 11t + 10 = 0$
    (d) $2a^2 = 17a - 30$ **(e)** $5y = 4y^2 - 6$ **(f)** $(x - 2)(x + 3) = 6$

Exercise 24vi

Links: 24G

What you should know

The solutions of the quadratic equation $ax^2 + bx + c = 0$ where $a \neq 0$ are given by the formula

$$x = \frac{-b \pm \sqrt{(b^2 - 4ac)}}{2a}$$

1 Use the quadratic formula to solve the following equations.
Give your answers correct to 3 significant figures.

(a) $x^2 + 4x + 2 = 0$

(b) $x^2 - 5x + 1 = 0$

(c) $y^2 - 6y - 5 = 0$

(d) $y^2 - 2y - 6 = 0$

(e) $2x^2 + 5x - 2 = 0$

(f) $3y^2 - 5y + 1 = 0$

(g) $3a^2 + 7a - 2 = 0$

(h) $4b^2 + b = 2$

(i) $5m^2 = 8m - 2$

Exercise 24vii

Links: 24H

What you should know

The discriminant is the expression $b^2 - 4ac$ under the square root sign in the quadratic formula.

If $b^2 - 4ac > 0$ there are two distinct solutions of the quadratic equation (if $b^2 - 4ac$ is a perfect square then the quadratic will factorise).

If $b^2 - 4ac = 0$ there is one solution (it is a repeated root).

If $b^2 - 4ac < 0$ there are no real solutions because you cannot find the square root of a negative number.

1 State whether these quadratic equations will have two, one or zero solutions.

(a) $x^2 + 6x - 2 = 0$

(b) $y^2 - 5y + 7 = 0$

(c) $4x^2 + 12x + 9 = 0$

(d) $3x^2 = 6x - 5$

(e) $10y = 5 - 2y^2$

(f) $5x = 6 + \dfrac{2}{x}$

Exercise 24viii

Links: 24I

What you should know

Completing the square means rewriting an expression of the form $x^2 + bx + c$ as $(x + p)^2 + q$.

The value of p is always half the value of b, the coefficient of x.

The value of q is found as in this example:

Put in the original number term.

$$x^2 - 6x + 2 = (x - 3)^2 - 3^2 + 2 = (x - 3)^2 - 9 + 2 = (x - 3)^2 - 7$$

p = half the coefficient of x.

Subtract p^2 (3^2).

1 Write these expressions in completed square form.

(a) $x^2 + 6x + 12$

(b) $y^2 + 10y - 4$

(c) $m^2 - 2m - 9$

(d) $p^2 - 12p + 15$

(e) $a^2 + 3a + 8$

(f) $b^2 - 5b - 6$

2 Write each of the following expressions in the form $(x + p)^2 + q$.
State clearly the values of p and q.

(a) $x^2 + 4x + 7$

(b) $x^2 - 6x - 5$

(c) $x^2 + 5x - 1$

(d) $x^2 - 7x + 16$

3 Solve these equations by completing the square.
Give your answers correct to 2 decimal places.

(a) $a^2 + 6a - 3 = 0$ (b) $b^2 - 8b + 14 = 0$ (c) $x^2 - 18x - 6 = 0$

4 Solve these equations by completing the square.
Leave your answers in the form $a \pm \sqrt{b}$, where a and b are integers.

(a) $x^2 - 6x - 13 = 0$ (b) $y^2 - 14y + 8 = 0$ (c) $w^2 + 12w - 4 = 0$

Exercise 24ix

Links: 24J

What you should know

To solve problems using quadratic equations, first set up the equation, reading the question carefully, then solve the equation.

Remember to state the answer to the question you were asked, explaining, if necessary, why one solution must be discounted.

---

1 The sum of the square of a number and ten times the number is 96. Find the two possible values of the number.

> In all of these questions you must show your working.

2 A rectangular field is 15 m longer than it is wide. If the area of the field is 1000 m², find the length and the width.

3 A rectangle has a perimeter of 42 cm.

  (a) If its width is x cm, write down an expression for its length in terms of x.

  (b) If the diagonal of the rectangle is 15 cm, form an equation in x and work out the dimensions of the rectangle.

4 A positive number minus five times its reciprocal is 8. Find the number, giving your answer correct to 3 s.f.

5 Find the lengths of the sides of this right-angled triangle. Give your answers correct to 2 d.p.

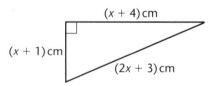

6 The diagrams show a rectangle and a square.
The area of the rectangle exceeds the area of the square by 12 cm².
Find the value of x, correct to 3 s.f.

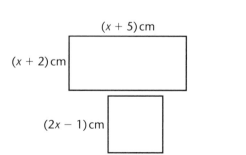

Mixed Exercise

1 Factorise

(a) $9b^2 - 49$

(b) $169q^2 - 36a$

(c) $100a^2 - 25x^2$

(d) $w^2 + 18w + 45$

(e) $t^2 + 9t - 22$

(f) $m^2 - 2m - 35$

(g) $p^2 - 17p + 60$

(h) $8n^2 + 18n - 35$

(i) $4a^2 + 18a - 36$

2 Solve the equation $3(t + 7)^2 = 24$ and give your answer to 3 s.f.

3 Solve the following quadratic equations.

(a) $w^2 + 11w - 26 = 0$

(b) $m^2 - 8m - 33 = 0$

(c) $k^2 + 19k - 20 = 0$

(d) $6h^2 + 23h - 4 = 0$

(e) $6b^2 - 23b + 20 = 0$

(f) $3t^2 = 5t + 12$

(g) $6p^2 - 7 = 2p$

(h) $3q^2 + 2 = 6q$

(i) $9s^2 - 2 = 9s$

4 Solve the following equations by completing the square.

(a) $2x^2 + 6 = x^2 - 6x$

(b) $3x^2 + 11x = 2x^2 + x - 12$

5 Two positive numbers have a difference of 7, and their squares have a sum of 337.

Let x be one of the numbers.

Write down an equation in x based on this information and solve it to find the two numbers.

Checklist

You should know how to...	Grade	For more help, look back at Student Book pages...
find the difference of two squares	B/A	428–429
factorise quadratic expressions	B/A	429–433
solve quadratic equations by rearranging and factorising	B/A	434–438
use the quadratic formula	A	438–439
find the discriminant	A*	439–440
complete the square	A*	440–443
solve problems using quadratic equations.	A*	444–447

Exercise 25i

Links: 25A

> **What you should know**
>
> In a non-linear function, the highest power of x is either less than or greater than 1. In a quadratic function, the highest power of x is x^2.
>
> Quadratic graphs are symmetrical about a line parallel to the y-axis. The general form of a quadratic function is given by $y = ax^2 + bx + c$, where a, b and c are constants called coefficients.
>
> All quadratic graphs are U-shaped or parabolic. The U-shape can be the right way up or upside down.

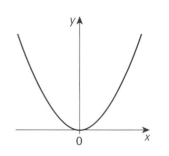

1 (a) Draw the graph of $y = 2x^2 + 3$ by completing the table of values given below.

x	-3	-2	-1	0	1	2	3
y	21			3			

(b) What is the equation of the line of symmetry?

2 (a) Construct a table of values for the equation $y = -3x^2 + 4$ between $x = -3$ and $x = +3$.

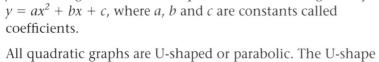
When the coefficient of x^2 is negative, the parabola is inverted.

(b) Plot the points and draw the graph.

(c) What would the graph of $y = 3x^2 + 4$ look like?

(d) What is the equation of the line of symmetry?

3 (a) Draw the graph of $y = 2x^2 - 4x - 8$ for values of x between -3 and $+5$.

(b) Show the line of symmetry and give its equation.

(c) Use your graph to find the solutions to the equation $2x^2 - 4x - 8 = 0$.

Exercise 25ii

Links: 25B

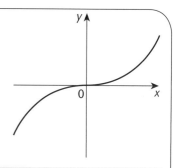

What you should know

A cubic function is one in which the highest power of x is x^3. The general form of a cubic equation is

$$y = ax^3 + bx^2 + cx + d.$$

Cubic graphs bend twice and all have rotational symmetry of order 2 about some particular point.

If the coefficient, a, is negative, the graph is inverted about the x-axis.

> The number of times a curved graph bends is always one less than its highest power.

1 (a) Copy and complete the table below for the cubic function $y = x^3 + 3x - 5$.

   (b) Plot the points and draw the graph.

   (c) Find the value of x where the curve crosses the x-axis.

x	-2	-1	0	1	2
x^3					
$+3x$					
-5					
y					

2 (a) Plot the graph of $y = x^3 + 4x^2 - 5x$ for x values between -6 and $+2$ by constructing a table of results.

   (b) Use your graph to estimate the solutions to the equation $x^3 + 4x^2 = 5x$.

3 Draw the graphs of the following cubic functions over the range of x indicated by constructing a table of values. For each graph state the values of x were the curve crosses the x-axis.

   (a) $y = x^3 + 2x^2 - x$ (-3 to 1)   (b) $y = -x^3 + 2$ (-2 to 2)

   (c) $y = \frac{1}{3}x^3 + \frac{1}{2}x^2$ (-3 to 2)   (d) $y = (x + 1)^3$ (-3 to 1)

Exercise 25iii

Links: 25C

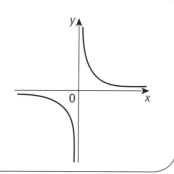

What you should know

A reciprocal function is one in which the power of x is x^{-1} or $\frac{1}{x}$. Reciprocal graphs have two asymptotes, i.e. a line or lines towards which the graph approaches but never reaches. The general expression for a reciprocal function is $y = \frac{a}{x}$, where a is a positive or negative constant.

1 (a) Copy and complete the table of values for the function $y = \frac{4}{x}$.

x	-3	-2	-1	1	2	3
y						

(b) Draw the graph over this range.

(c) What are the equations of the asymptotes?

2 (a) Draw a graph of the function $y = -\frac{3}{x} + 2$ over the range of x values between -4 and $+4$ by constructing a table of results. Include the points -0.5 and 0.5.

(b) Draw the asymptotes and give their equations.

3 (a) Draw the reciprocal graph $y = 3 - \frac{5}{x}$ between x values -4 and $+4$.

(b) Give the equations of the two asymptotes.

4 (a) Draw the graph of the function $xy = 6$ over the range of x values between -4 and $+4$.

(b) Give the equations of the asymptotes.

Exercise 25iv

Links: 25D

> ### What you should know
>
> An exponential function is a function of the form $y = a^x$, where a is a positive number. They are always positive and always pass through the point $(0, 1)$.
>
> The inverse function $y = a^{-x}$ is simply a reflection in the y-axis of the function $y = a^x$.

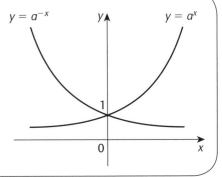

1 (a) Copy and complete the table for the exponential function $y = 0.8^x$, giving your values to 2 d.p.

x	-5	-4	-3	-2	-1	0	1	2	3	4	5
y											

(b) Draw the graph of this function.

2 (a) Copy and complete the table below for the function $y = (3.7)^{-x}$
for the x values shown.

x	-1	0	1	2	3	4
y						

(b) Plot the points and draw the graph.

3 A particular water algae grows exponentially during the
summer months. Its population is described by the function
$p = a \times 3.4^{\frac{t}{10}}$, where a is the population at the start and t is
the time in days.

> Remember to include x
> values close to zero but
> do not include zero itself if
> the combination function
> contains a reciprocal term.

(a) Work out the population after 5 days when $a = 50$.

(b) Draw a graph of the population increase between $t = 0$ and
$t = 20$ using the values of t of 0, 5, 10, 15 and 20.

(c) From the graph, work out the time taken to double the population.

Exercise 25v

Links: 25E

> ### What you should know
>
> Combination functions involve linear, quadratic, cubic and/or reciprocal terms. These are
> best drawn by tabulating the results first.

1 (a) Copy and complete the table for the function $y = x - \dfrac{3}{x}$
between the x values -4 and $+4$.

x	-4	-3	-2	-1	-0.5	-0.2	0.2	0.5	1	2	3	4
$-\dfrac{3}{x}$												
y												

(b) Plot the points and draw the graph.

(c) Draw the asymptotes and give the equations of these
asymptotes.

2 (a) Copy and complete the table below for the function $y = x^3 - \dfrac{1}{x} + 2$.

x	-2	-1	-0.5	-0.2	0.2	0.5	1	2
x^3								
$-\dfrac{1}{x}$								
$+2$								
y								

(b) Draw the graph of the function and give the equation of one of the asymptotes.

Exercise 25vi

Links: 25F

> ### What you should know
>
> Quadratic equations can be solved graphically by finding the points of intersection of these graphs with either the x-axis or with other linear graphs.
>
> Sometimes it is necessary to rearrange an equation into two parts to so that one of the parts is in the form of the original quadratic function.

1 Draw the graph of $y = 3x - 2$ for x values between -2 and $+3$. It intersects the line $y = 1.6$ at the point P. What are the coordinates of P?

Accurate drawings are needed if good solutions are to be obtained.

2 (a) Copy and complete the table for the quadratic function $y = 2x^2 - 4$.

x	-3	-2	-1	0	1	2	3
y							

  (b) Draw this curve and find where it crosses the x-axis.
  (c) Draw the line $y = 10$ on the same graph.
  (d) Write down the coordinates of the points of intersection.

3 (a) Draw the graph of $y = x^2 - 3x - 4$ for x values between -3 and $+6$.
  (b) Draw the line $y = 6$ on the same graph.
  (c) Write down the x values of the points of intersection of the curve and the line.
  (d) Write an equation that is solved by these x values.
  (e) Use your graph to solve the equation $x^2 - 3x - 4 = 0$.

4 (a) Draw the graph of the function $y = 2x^2 + x - 6$ for x values between -3 and $+3$.
  (b) Use your graph to find the solution of the equation $2x^2 + x - 6 = 0$.
  (c) By drawing an appropriate straight line write down the solutions to the equation $2x^2 - 2x - 4 = 0$.

Exercise 25vii

Links: 25G

> ### What you should know
>
> You should be able to recognise the shape and properties of linear and non-linear graphs and be able to sketch and to know how to interpret them and what they represent.
>
> Often the shape of a container to be filled will reflect some of the properties of the graph.

1 Look at the following list of functions. Describe the graph of the function as either linear (L), quadratic (Q), cubic (C), reciprocal (R), exponential (E) or a combination (T).

(a) $y = \frac{1}{x} + 3$

(b) $y = 3x^3 + 2x - 7$

(c) $y = 6^x$

(d) $y = -3x^2 + 4x - 9$

(e) $xy = 9$

(f) $2x + 3y = 7$

(g) $3 - \frac{5}{x} = y$

(h) $y = 2x^3 - \frac{1}{x} + 2$

2 Match each equation to one of the graphs A–E below.

(a) $xy = -2$

(b) $y = 10^x$

(c) $y = 2 - 3x^2$

(d) $3x + 2y = 10$

(e) $y = x^3 + 3x - 1$

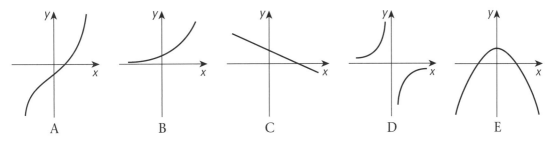

A   B   C   D   E

3 Water is poured into the following vases at a constant rate. Sketch a graph to show how the volume of water changes with height.

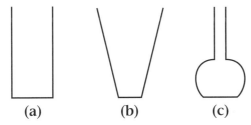

(a)   (b)   (c)

Mixed Exercise

1 (a) Copy and complete the table of values for $y = 3x^2 - 5x - 2$.

x	−1	0	1	2	3
y					

(b) Draw the graph and use this to find the solutions to the equation $3x^2 - 5x - 2 = 0$.

(c) Draw the line $y = 2x - 1$ on the same graph and write down the x coordinates of the points of intersection.

(d) Using the information to part (c), write down and simplify an equation that has these x values as the solution.

2 (a) Construct a table of results for the function $y = (0.2)^{2x}$ for
  x values $-0.5, -0.2, -0.1, 0, 0.1, 0.2, 0.5, 1$ and 1.5.

  (b) Plot these points and draw the graph.

  (c) Use your graph to solve the equation $(0.2)^{2x} = 3$ giving
  your answer to 2 d.p.

3 A stone is dropped down a well. Its depth, d, at any time t,
  is given by the function $d = 5t^2$. Which of the graphs below
  best describes how the depth changes with time?

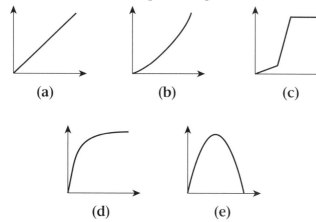

Checklist

You should know how to...	Grade	For more help, look back at Student Book pages...
recognise linear, quadratic and cubic graphs by inspection	D to A	450–455
recognise both reciprocal and exponential graphs and use their associated properties	A/A*	455–460
solve quadratic equations graphically	C to A	461–466
apply graphs to solving 'realistic' problems.	A/A*	467–469

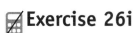

Exercise 26i

26A, 26B

What you should know

To turn a terminating decimal into a fraction, look at the place value of the last significant digit and write the fraction with this denominator.

To turn a recurring decimal into a fraction, multiply both sides by 10 if one digit recurs, by 100 if two digits recur, etc. then subtract to leave only integers. Sometimes you might need two multiplications.

To turn a fraction into a decimal, divide the numerator by the denominator.

1 Change these fractions into decimals. State whether they are recurring, terminating or non-terminating decimals.

(a) $\frac{3}{8}$ (b) $\frac{5}{9}$ (c) $\frac{9}{25}$ (d) $\frac{5}{12}$ (e) $\frac{8}{17}$

Terminating decimal
$0.65 = \frac{65}{100}$. The place value of the last digit tells you the denominator.

2 Find fractions that are equivalent to the following terminating decimals. Give your answer in its simplest form.

(a) 0.76   (b) 0.625   (c) 0.004

Recurring decimal.
Let $x = 0.444\ldots$
$10x = 4.444\ldots$
$-x = -0.444\ldots$
$9x = 4$
$x = \frac{4}{9}$

3 Find the fractions that are equivalent to the following recurring decimals.

(a) 0.444...   (b) 0.363636...   (c) 0.726726...

(d) 0.8333...   (e) 0.00848484... (f) 0.6777...

4 Sally thinks $\frac{7}{9}$ is closer to $\frac{4}{5}$ than $\frac{3}{4}$. Jane thinks its the other way round. Who is correct?

Exercise 26ii

Links 26C, 26D

What you should know

A rational number is one that can be written in the form $\frac{a}{b}$ where a and b are integers and $b \neq 0$. An irrational number is one that cannot be written in this way.

Surds are irrational numbers written in a form using square roots and cube roots. Use the following rules to manipulate surds.

$$\sqrt{a} \times \sqrt{b} = \sqrt{ab}$$

$$\frac{\sqrt{a}}{\sqrt{b}} = \sqrt{\frac{a}{b}}$$

$$m\sqrt{a} \times n\sqrt{b} = mn\sqrt{ab}$$

$$m\sqrt{a} \div n\sqrt{b} = \frac{m}{n}\sqrt{\frac{a}{b}}$$

$$m\sqrt{a} + n\sqrt{a} = (m+n)\sqrt{a}$$

1 For each of the following state whether they are rational or irrational numbers.

   (a) $\sqrt{10}$ **(b)** $\frac{3}{8}$ **(c)** 0.44...   **(d)** $\sqrt{49}$ **(e)** π

> An irrational number does not terminate or make a recurring pattern.

2 Find the length of the side *AB*. Give your answer in surd form.

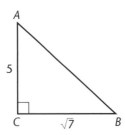

3 Simplify these expressions, leaving your answers in surd form where applicable.

   (a) $\sqrt{8} \times \sqrt{8}$ **(b)** $\sqrt{6} \times \sqrt{3}$ **(c)** $\sqrt{60} \div \sqrt{15}$

   (d) $2\sqrt{7} \times 2\sqrt{8}$ **(e)** $8\sqrt{6} \div 4\sqrt{3}$ **(f)** $5\sqrt{7} \times 3\sqrt{7}$

4 Write each of the following surds in the form $a\sqrt{b}$.

   (a) $\sqrt{28}$ **(b)** $\sqrt{125}$ **(c)** $\sqrt{63}$ **(d)** $\sqrt{600}$

5 Simplify the following, leaving your answers in surd form.

   (a) $\sqrt{\dfrac{27}{32}}$ **(b)** $\sqrt{\dfrac{24}{30}}$ **(c)** $\sqrt{\dfrac{175}{150}}$ **(d)** $\sqrt{\dfrac{32}{98}}$

6 Simplify   **(a)** $\sqrt{50} + \sqrt{18}$ **(b)** $\sqrt{12} + \sqrt{48}$ **(c)** $\sqrt{162} - \sqrt{72}$.

7 Find   **(a)** the perimeter
         (b) the area
         (c) the length of the diagonal.

Exercise 26iii

Links: 26E, 26F

> ### What you should know
>
> When the denominator of a fraction is a surd, remove the surd from the denominator by multiplying the top and bottom of the fractions by the appropriate square root. This is called rationalising the denominator.

1 Simplify   **(a)** $\dfrac{1}{\sqrt{3}}$ **(b)** $\dfrac{10}{\sqrt{2}}$ **(c)** $\dfrac{1}{2\sqrt{5}}$ **(d)** $\dfrac{\sqrt{2}}{\sqrt{8}}$.

2 Multiply these fractions, simplifying your answers.

   (a) $\dfrac{1}{\sqrt{5}} \times \dfrac{1}{\sqrt{6}}$ **(b)** $\dfrac{4}{\sqrt{3}} \times \dfrac{3}{\sqrt{7}}$ **(c)** $\dfrac{\sqrt{2}}{\sqrt{5}} \times \dfrac{\sqrt{2}}{\sqrt{8}}$.

3 Find the area of a circle with a radius of $\dfrac{5}{\sqrt{3}}$.

4 The area of a parallelogram is 30 cm². If the height is $\sqrt{20}$ cm, what will be the length of the base? Give your answer in surd form.

Mixed Exercise

1 Find the fractions that are equivalent to

    (a) 0.015   **(b)** 0.888   **(c)** 0.2828...

2 Which of the following are irrational numbers?

    $\sqrt{36}$ $\frac{4}{9}$ 0.275 π $\sqrt{7}$

3 Simplify   **(a)** $\sqrt{24} \div \sqrt{8}$ **(b)** $2\sqrt{5} \times 3\sqrt{7}$ **(c)** $\dfrac{1}{\sqrt{5}}$.

4 Write the following in the form $a\sqrt{b}$.

    (a) $\sqrt{8}$ **(b)** $\sqrt{54}$ **(c)** $\sqrt{250}$

5 **(a)** Find the area of this isosceles triangle.

    (b) Find the length of AB.

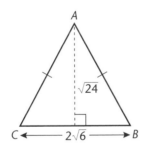

Checklist

You should know how to....	Grade	For more help, look back at Student Book pages...
convert terminating and recurring decimals into fractions	C to A	473–477
identify rational and irrational numbers	A	473
simplify surds	A/A*	478–481
rationalise the denominator	A/A*	481–482

Exercise 27i

What you should know

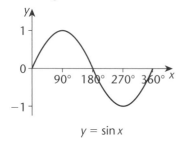

$y = \sin x$

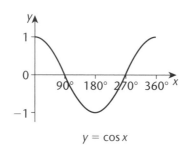

$y = \cos x$

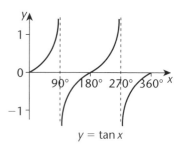

$y = \tan x$

You can use the symmetry properties of the trigonometric functions to work out equivalent angles over the range $-360°$ to $360°$. The period of both sine and cosine is $360°$ but is only $180°$ for tangent.

 1 Find two angles in the range $0° \leqslant x \leqslant 360°$ that satisfy each of the following equations.

> Give you answers correct to one decimal place.

   (a) $\sin x = 0.35$ **(b)** $\cos x = -0.71$ **(c)** $\tan x = 5.8$

 2 Work out the following to 1 d.p. in the range $-180° \leqslant x \leqslant 180°$.

   (a) $\sin x = 0.83$ **(b)** $\cos x = -0.18$ **(c)** $\tan x = 25.6$

   (d) $\sin x = -0.22$ **(e)** $\tan x = -67$ **(f)** $\cos x = 0.96$

3 (a) Plot the graph of $y = \cos x$ between $-180°$ and $+180°$.

   (b) From your graph find the angle that is equivalent to $\cos x = 0.79$ (give your answer to the nearest degree).

   (c) The curve is symmetrical about what angle?

 4 (a) Copy and complete the following table of values for $\sin x$.

x	$-180°$	$-90°$	$-45°$	$0°$	$45°$	$90°$	$180°$
$\sin x$			-0.707			1	

   (b) Plot these points on graph paper and join the points with a smooth continuous curve.

   (c) From your graph find the angles that are given by $\sin x = \pm 0.2$ (to 1 d.p.)

Exercise 27ii

Links: 27A

What you should know

Trigonometric equations are equations involving trigonometric functions of the form $\sin x = p$, $\cos x = q$ and $\tan x = r$.

The symmetry of the graphs enables you to read off certain key results.

Positive regions can be easily identified from this diagram.

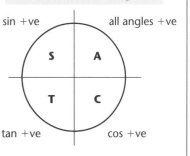

$\sin x = \sin(360 + x)$, $\sin(180 - x) = \sin x$, $\sin(-x) = -\sin x$

$\cos x = \cos(360 + x)$, $\cos(180 - x) = -\cos x$, $\cos(-x) = \cos x$

$\tan x = \tan(180 + x)$, $\tan(180 - x) = -\tan x$, $\tan(-x) = -\tan x$

1. Find all the solutions to the equation $\cos x = 0.3$ in the range $0° \leqslant x \leqslant 360°$, giving your answer correct to 1 d.p.

2. Given that $\cos 27° = 0.891$,
   (a) find all the values of x in the range $-360° \leqslant x \leqslant 360°$ that satisfies the equation $\cos x = 0.891$
   (b) find all the solutions of the equation $\sin x = 0.891$ in this range, correct to the nearest degree.

3. Solve the equation $8\sin x = -1$ in the range $0° \leqslant x \leqslant 360°$, correct to 1 d.p.

Execise 27iii

Links: 27B

What you should know

You can use these right-angled triangles to work out sin, cos and tan of 30°, 45° and 60° in surd form.

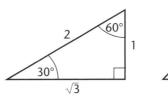
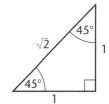

1. The top of a tree is to be measured a distance of 5 m away from its base. The angle of elevation is 60°. How tall is the tree? Leave your answer in surd form.

2. A square piece of wood has a side length of 15 cm. Using the fact that $\cos 45° = \dfrac{1}{\sqrt{2}}$, work out the length of the diagonal. Leave your answer in terms of $\sqrt{2}$.

3 In this triangle the tangent of the angle is $\frac{3}{5}$. Work out the values of cos x and sin x, leaving your answers in surd form.

4 *ABCD* is a trapezium with *BC* = 3 cm as shown. Work out the length of *AD*, leaving your answer in surd form.

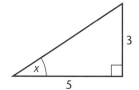

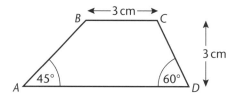

▦ Exercise 27iv

Links: 27C

What you should know

Area of a triangle $ABC = \frac{1}{2}ab \sin C$

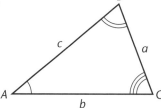

By symmetry,
area $ABC = \frac{1}{2}ac \sin B$
area $ABC = \frac{1}{2}ab \sin c$
are also true.

1 Find the area of each triangle, giving your answers to 1 d.p.

(a)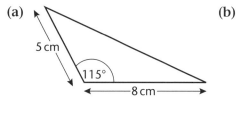

(b)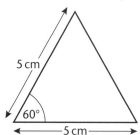

2 *PQRS* is a parallelogram with *PQ* = 12 cm and *QR* = 18 cm. If the angle *PQR* = 135°, work out the area of the parallelogram *PQRS* correct to 3 s.f.

3 A triangular section of land *ABC* is to be fenced. If *AB* = 75 m, *AC* = 122 m and the angle *CAB* = 104°, work out the area of the land enclosed by the fence. Give your answer correct to 4 s.f.

4 A square-based pyramid has a base length of 4 cm. The slant height of the four triangles is 6 cm and the angle at the tip of the triangles is 25°. Work out the total surface area of the net of this shape to 1 d.p.

Exercise 27v

Links: 27D

What you should know

Area of a segment = area of sector − area of triangle

$$= \frac{\theta}{360} \times \pi r^2 - \frac{1}{2}r^2\sin\theta$$

1 Find the area of the minor segments cut off by the chords in the following circles.

(a)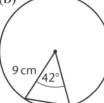
85°
6 cm

(b) 9 cm
42°

(c)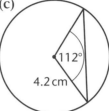
112°
4.2 cm

2 On the walls of ancient Egyptian temples they covered the cutting segment of the Pharaoh's axes with gold.

   (a) Find the area covered by gold.

   (b) If the gold is 1 mm thick, what is the volume of gold?

   (c) Gold has a density of 13.2 g/cm³. What is the mass of gold?

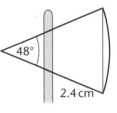
48°
2.4 cm

Exercise 27vi

Links: 27E

What you should know

Sine rule: $\dfrac{a}{\sin A} = \dfrac{b}{\sin B} = \dfrac{c}{\sin C}$ This formula is given to you at the start of an exam paper.

It is easier to rearrange the formula so that the unknown quantity is the numerator.

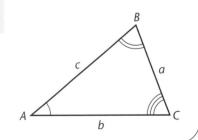

1 In the triangle ABC, find the length of AC

   (a) in surd form   **(b)** correct to 3 s.f.

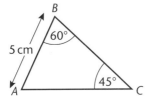
60°
5 cm
45°

2 In the triangle *PQR* find the size of the angle marked *x*

(a) in surd form

(b) correct to 3 s.f.

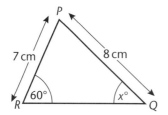

3 From a port *P*, boat *A* is 3 km away on a bearing of 220° and boat *B* is 2 km away on a bearing of 165°. Calculate the distance between the boats.

4 Point *B* is 9 km north of point *A*. Point *C* is 8 km from *B* and 5 km from *A*, lying to the east of the line *AB*.

(a) Draw triangle *ABC* and calculate angle *BAC*.

(b) If *C* now moves until it is due east of *A*, how far does it move?

⊞ Exercise 27vii

Links: 27F

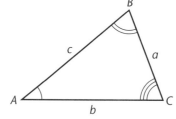

What you should know

Cosine rule: $a^2 = b^2 + c^2 - 2bc \cos A$

$$\cos A = \frac{b^2 + c^2 - a^2}{2bc}$$

When angle A is a right angle, cos A = 0 and the expression reduces to $a^2 = b^2 + c^2$. This is just Pythagoras' theorem.

1 In a triangle *XYZ*, *XY* = 6 cm, *YZ* = 5 cm and angle *XYZ* = 55°. Find the length of *XZ* to 3 s.f.

2 In the triangle *ABC* shown below find

(a) angle *ABC*

(b) angle *CAB*, correct to the nearest degree. Hence find angle *ACB*.

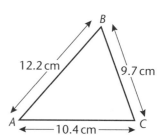

3   An astronomer is making observations of two stars that are
    known to be 45 and 165 light years away. The telescope
    moves through an angle of 2.72° to go from one star to the
    other. How far apart are the stars? Give your answer to the
    nearest light year.

4   A yacht takes two bearings from the same lighthouse on its
    voyage parallel to the coastline. The first bearing is 33.8° when
    4.6 km away, and 071° when 15.7 km away from the lighthouse.
    How far has the yacht travelled between these two bearings?

Mixed Exercise

1   Solve the equation $5\cos x = 2$, giving all answers to 1 d.p. in
    the range $-180° \leqslant x \leqslant 180°$.

2   In the triangle ABC find the length BX using surds. Do not
    use a calculator. You must show your working.

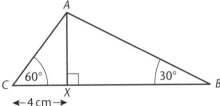

3   Find the area of the triangle PQR.

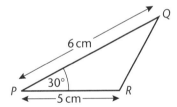

4   A small fishing boat sails from a port, P, for 10 km on a
    bearing of 060° and then sails for 8 km on a bearing of 165°.
    What is the distance and bearing of the boat from P?

Checklist

You should know how to...	Grade	For more help, look back at Student Book pages...
draw graphs of sine, cosine and tangent	A	487–491
solve trigonomtric equations using the symmetry properties of the trigonomtric graphs	A/A*	491–497
work out areas of triangles and segments of circles using trigonometric expressions	A/A*	497–500
use the sine and cosine rules.	A/A*	501–505

Exercise 28i

Links: 28A

What you should know

To solve one linear and one quadratic simultaneous equation you need to use the method of substitution to find values of x and y that satisfy both equations simultaneously.

Find the points of intersection of these quadratic and straight-line graphs.

1 $y = x + 9$
  $y = x^2 - 3$

2 $y = x + 5$
  $y = x^2 - 25$

3 $y = 3x$
  $y = x2 + 10x - 8$

4 $y = x - 2$
  $y = x^2 - 2x - 20$

5 $y = 5x + 1$
  $y = x^2 + 7$

6 $y = 6x + 5$
  $y = x^2 + 4x - 3$

7 $y = 2 - 7x$
  $y = x^2 + 8$

8 $y = 4x + 5$
  $y^2 = 8x + 9$

Exercise 28ii

Links: 28B

What you should know

The equation of a circle with centre $(0, 0)$ and radius r is $x^2 + y^2 = r^2$.

Find the points of intersection of these straight lines and circles.

1 $x^2 + y^2 = 5$
  $y = x - 1$

2 $x^2 + y^2 = 10$
  $y = x + 2$

3 $x^2 + y^2 = 13$
  $y = x - 5$

4 $x^2 + y^2 = 17$
  $y = x + 3$

5 $x^2 + y^2 = 40$
  $y = x - 4$

Determine whether the circle and the straight line have **(a)** 2 **(b)** 1 **(c)** 0 points of intersection in each of the following. You must show your working.

6 $x^2 + y^2 = 12$
  $y = x + 5$

7 $x^2 + y^2 = 20$
  $y = x - 4$

8 $x^2 + y^2 = 98$
  $y = x + 14$

Exercise 28iii

Links: 28C

What you should know

To simplify algebraic fractions:

(1) factorise

(2) divide by the HCF (or cancel common factors).

Simplify the following, where possible.

1 $\dfrac{4x - 10}{2}$ **2** $\dfrac{3x - 7}{6}$ **3** $\dfrac{6y}{3y + 9}$

4 $\dfrac{8 - 2f}{4f}$ **5** $\dfrac{2p}{4q}$ **6** $\dfrac{6p^2q}{2p}$

7 $\dfrac{3p + q}{p + q}$ **8** $\dfrac{4t^2 + 6t}{10t^2}$ **9** $\dfrac{x^2 + 3x - 40}{x - 5}$

10 $\dfrac{x^2 + 8x - 9}{x + 9}$ **11** $\dfrac{y + 2}{y^2 - 5y - 14}$ **12** $\dfrac{2x^2 + 3x - 14}{5x^2 - 9x - 2}$

Exercise 28iv

Links: 28D

What you should know

The rules for multiplying algebraic fractions are exactly the same as for numerical fractions, but always remember to look for any factors before you simplify.

Work out the following, simplifying your answers.

1 $\dfrac{a}{6} \times \dfrac{b}{2}$ **2** $\dfrac{m}{n} \div \dfrac{4}{n}$ **3** $\dfrac{5t}{4} \times \dfrac{8}{t^2}$

4 $\dfrac{h^2}{k} \div \dfrac{3h}{k^2}$ **5** $\dfrac{8p}{10q^2} \div \dfrac{2p^2}{5q}$ **6** $\dfrac{9x - 3}{y} \times \dfrac{2y}{3x - 1}$

7 $\dfrac{x^2 - 3x}{x^2 + x} \times \dfrac{2x + 2}{4}$ **8** $\dfrac{5m + 10}{y^3} \div \dfrac{3m + 6}{y^2}$

9 $\dfrac{k^2 - 49}{k^2 - k - 42} \times \dfrac{k^2 + 8k + 12}{4k + 28}$ **10** $\dfrac{4t^2 - 1}{2t^2 - 5t - 3} \div \dfrac{2t^2 + 11t - 6}{2t^2 - 18}$

Exercise 28v

Links: 28E

> **What you should know**
>
> The rules for adding and subtracting algebraic fractions are the same as for numerical fractions, but before you find the LCM you must factorise the numerators and/or denominators if possible.

Simplify the following.

1 $\dfrac{3x}{7} + \dfrac{x}{7}$

2 $\dfrac{2y}{5} - \dfrac{y}{4}$

3 $\dfrac{1}{5x} - \dfrac{2}{3x^2}$

4 $\dfrac{x + 3}{2} + \dfrac{x - 1}{3}$

5 $\dfrac{y - 5}{4} - \dfrac{y + 1}{7}$

6 $\dfrac{3m + 1}{4} - \dfrac{2m + 5}{7}$

Exercise 28vi

Links: 28F

Solve these equations.

1 $\dfrac{x}{2} + \dfrac{x + 1}{3} = 7$

2 $\dfrac{x - 1}{3} + \dfrac{x + 2}{4} = -1$

3 $\dfrac{x - 2}{5} - \dfrac{x - 3}{3} = 1$

4 $\dfrac{2x - 1}{5} + \dfrac{x + 3}{2} = 4$

5 $\dfrac{2x + 1}{4} - \dfrac{x + 1}{3} = -1.5$

6 $\dfrac{5x - 3}{2} - \dfrac{4x - 1}{6} = 6$

7 $\dfrac{4}{x + 2} + \dfrac{1}{x - 1} = 2$

8 $\dfrac{10}{x + 4} - \dfrac{9}{x + 2} = -1$

9 $\dfrac{3}{2x + 1} + \dfrac{4}{x + 5} = -2$

Exercise 28vii

Links: 28G

> **What you should know**
>
> To change the subject of a formula, follow this order of operations:
> (1) Square both sides
> (2) Multiply through by...
> (3) Expand
> (4) Rearrange
> (5) Factorise
> (6) Divide through by...
> (7) Square root both sides

Make a the subject of these formulae.

1 $\dfrac{Xa + B}{M} = k$

2 $\dfrac{t - Da}{c} = P$

3 $f(Na - t) = Q$

4 $\dfrac{V(h - a)}{E} = m$ **5** $\dfrac{hv - a^2}{3} = y$ **6** $R = \sqrt{n - 2a}$

7 $4a - b = ka + c$ **8** $\sqrt{\dfrac{a + c}{a - c}} = h$ **9** $\sqrt{\dfrac{y(a^2 + 3)}{e}} = w$

Mixed Exercise

1 Find the points of intersection of these quadratic and straight-line graphs.

(a) $y = 2x - 7$
     $y^2 = 6x - 11$

(b) $5y = x - 14$
     $y^2 = 2x + 11$

2 Find the points of intersection of this straight line and circle.
$x^2 + y^2 = 50$
$y = x + 6$

3 Simplify where possible.

(a) $\dfrac{5n}{10mn^2}$

(b) $\dfrac{w^2 - 64}{w^2 + 4w - 32}$

4 Work out the following, simplifying your answers.

(a) $\dfrac{6w + 18}{4w - 2} \times \dfrac{2w - 1}{w^2 + w - 6}$

(b) $\dfrac{5m + 35}{m^2 + 2m - 3} \div \dfrac{m^2 + 3m - 28}{4m + 12}$

5 Simplify

(a) $\dfrac{3}{2p} + \dfrac{2}{pq}$

(b) $\dfrac{2x + 1}{5} + \dfrac{x - 6}{2}$

6 Solve the equation $\dfrac{9}{2x - 3} + \dfrac{2}{x - 4} = 1$.

7 Make a the subject of the following formulae.

(a) $C - \dfrac{d}{a} = H$ (b) $p(a + q) = 2t - a$ (c) $\dfrac{a + b}{a + f} = \dfrac{t}{n}$

Checklist

You should know how to...	Grade	For more help, look back at Student Book pages...
solve simultaneous equations, one linear and one quadratic	A/A*	508–511
find points of intersection of a circle and a straight line	A/A*	511–512
simplify and manipulate algebraic fractions	A/A*	513–519
change the subject of a formula.	A/A*	519–521

Exercise 29i

Links: 29A

What you should know

$y = x + 6$, $f(x) = x + 6$ and $f: x \to x + 6$ are three different ways of expressing the same x–y relationship.

1 $f(x) = 2x^2 - 5$

    (a) Find the values of

        (i) $f(6)$ **(ii)** $f(-3)$ **(iii)** $f(0)$ **(iv)** $f(1.5)$.

    (b) Find the values of x for which

        (i) $f(x) = 27$ **(ii)** $f(x) = -4.5$ **(iii)** $f(x) = 9x$.

2 $f(x) = 3x^2 + x - 2$

    (a) Find the values of

        (i) $f(0)$ **(ii)** $f(4)$ **(iii)** $f(-5)$ **(iv)** $f(0.5)$.

    (b) Find the values of x for which

        (i) $f(x) = 0$ **(ii)** $f(x) = 2$ **(iii)** $f(x) = 22$.

Exercise 29ii

Links: 29B

What you should know

$y = f(x) \to y = f(x) + a$ represents a translation of $\begin{pmatrix} 0 \\ a \end{pmatrix}$.

$y = f(x) \to y = f(x + a)$ represents a translation of $\begin{pmatrix} -a \\ 0 \end{pmatrix}$.

1 Draw axes $-4 \leqslant x \leqslant 4$ and $-5 \leqslant y \leqslant 20$ and plot the graph of $y = x^2$.
On the same axes, draw the graph of

    (a) $y = x^2 + 4$ **(b)** $y = x^2 - 3$
    (c) $y = (x - 3)^2$ **(d)** $y = (x + 2)^2$.

State clearly in each case how the graph is obtained from the graph of $y = x^2$.

2 Write down the equation of the graph that can be obtained from the graph of $y = x^3$ by a translation of

    (a) $\begin{pmatrix} 0 \\ 7 \end{pmatrix}$ **(b)** $\begin{pmatrix} 5 \\ 0 \end{pmatrix}$ **(c)** $\begin{pmatrix} -1 \\ 0 \end{pmatrix}$ **(d)** $\begin{pmatrix} 0 \\ -6 \end{pmatrix}$.

Exercise 29iii

Links: 29C

> ## What you should know
>
> $y = f(x) \rightarrow y = af(x)$ represents a one-way stretch from the x-axis parallel to the y-axis of scale factor a.
> $y = f(x) \rightarrow y = f(ax)$ represents a one-way stretch from the y-axis parallel to the x-axis of scale factor $\frac{1}{a}$.

1 Describe the transformation that maps $y = x^3$ onto each of these graphs.

   (a) $y = 2x^3$ **(b)** $y = (2x)^3$

   (c) $y = \frac{1}{4}x^3$ **(d)** $y = \left(\frac{1}{4}x\right)^3$

2 Write down the equation of the graph that can be obtained from the graph of $y = x^3$ by a transformation of

   (a) a one-way stretch from the x-axis parallel to the y-axis of scale factor **(i)** 3   **(ii)** 1.5   **(iii)** $\frac{1}{2}$.

   (b) a one-way stretch from the y-axis parallel to the x-axis of scale factor **(i)** $\frac{1}{6}$ **(ii)** 3   **(iii)** 2.5.

Exercise 29iv

Links: 29D

> ## What you should know
>
> $y = -f(x)$ is a reflection of $y = f(x)$ in the x-axis.
> $y = f(-x)$ is a reflection of $y = f(x)$ in the y-axis.

1 Draw the graph of the straight line $y = \frac{1}{2}x + 2$ for values of x from -4 to 4.

   (a) Reflect the graph of $y = \frac{1}{2}x + 2$ in the x-axis and write the equation of the reflected graph in its simplest form.

   (b) Reflect the graph of $y = \frac{1}{2}x + 2$ in the y-axis and write the equation of the reflected graph in its simplest form.

2 Write down, in their simplest form, the equations of these graphs when they are reflected in **(i)** the x-axis **(ii)** the y-axis.

   (a) $y = 3x - 1$ **(b)** $y = 4 - \frac{1}{2}x$

   (c) $y = x^2 - 5x$ **(d)** $y = x^3 - 3$

   (e) $y = 5x^2 + x$ **(f)** $y = 2x^2 - 4x + 1$

You do *not* need to draw the graphs.

3 Copy the graph of this function, $y = f(x)$.
On the same axes, draw the graphs of

(a) $y = f(x) + 7$ (b) $y = 2f(x)$

(c) $y = -f(x)$ (d) $y = f(-x)$

(e) $y = f(-x) - 5$ (f) $y = f(x + 4)$

(g) $y = f(x - 6)$.

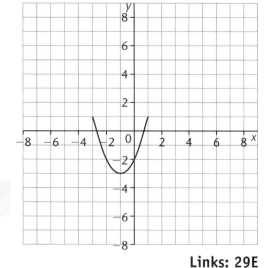

> Work out what transformation the equation represents before you draw the graph.

Exercise 29v

Links: 29E

1 For each of these graphs
  (i) complete the square of the function
  (ii) describe how the graph is obtained from $y = x^2$
  (iii) draw a sketch graph to illustrate your answer.

(a) $y = x^2 + 4x - 4$ (b) $y = x^2 - 2x + 7$

(c) $y = x^2 + 6x + 13$ (d) $y = x^2 - 12x + 35$

2 Describe the combination of transformations that takes the graph of $y = x^2$ onto each of these graphs.

For each one, draw a sketch graph to illustrate your answer.

(a) $y = (x + 1)^2 - 4$ (b) $y = (x - 2)^2 + 5$

(c) $y = 3x^2 - 2$ (d) $y = 2(x + 4)^2$

(e) $y = -x^2 - 4$ (f) $y = 6 - 2x^2$

3 In each of these, the graph of $y = x^2$ is transformed into another graph by the given transformations carried out in the order stated.

For each one, draw sketch graphs to illustrate *each stage* of the transformation.

Deduce the equation of the graph *after each stage*.

(a)   (i) A translation of $\binom{3}{0}$.

    (ii) A reflection in the x-axis.

    (iii) A translation of $\binom{0}{-2}$.

(b)   (i) A translation of $\binom{-2}{0}$.

    (ii) A one-way stretch from the x-axis parallel to the y-axis of scale factor 2.

    (iii) A reflection in the x-axis.

(c) **(i)** A translation of $\begin{pmatrix} -5 \\ 0 \end{pmatrix}$.

    (ii) A reflection in the x-axis.

    (iii) A one-way stretch from the x-axis parallel to the y-axis of scale factor 2.

    (iv) A translation of $\begin{pmatrix} 0 \\ 3 \end{pmatrix}$.

(d) **(i)** A reflection in the x-axis.

    (ii) A one-way stretch from the y-axis parallel to the x-axis of scale factor $\frac{1}{2}$.

    (iii) A translation of $\begin{pmatrix} 0 \\ 4 \end{pmatrix}$.

Exercise 29vi

Links: 29F

What you should know

The period of a trigonometric graph is the number of degrees after which it repeats itself.

The amplitude is the maximum height of the waveform above the x-axis.

1 Draw sketch graphs to show each of these transformations of the graphs of $y = \sin x$ or $y = \cos x$.

    (i) For each one, start by drawing $y = \sin x$ or $y = \cos x$, then draw the transformed graph *on the same axes*, using values of x in the range $-90° \leqslant x \leqslant 450°$.

    (ii) Describe each transformation in words.

    (iii) State the period and amplitude of each transformed graph.

(a) $y = \sin x \rightarrow y = -\sin x$

(b) $y = \cos x \rightarrow y = \cos x + 2$

(c) $y = \sin x \rightarrow y = \sin (x + 90°)$

(d) $y = \cos x \rightarrow y = 2 \cos (x - 90°)$

(e) $y = \sin x \rightarrow y = 3 \sin x - 1$

Two transformations. What are they?

(f) $y = \cos x \rightarrow y = -\frac{1}{2} \cos x + 1$

Three transformations. What are they?

Exercise 29vii

Links: 29G

> **What you should know**
>
> You can use the symmetry properties of the graphs of $y = \sin x$ and $y = \cos x$ to solve simple trigonomic equations.

1 You are given that $\cos 41° = 0.7547$.
Draw the graph of $y = \cos x$ for $0° \leqslant x \leqslant 360°$ and use it to find values of x in this range for which
   (a) $\cos x = 0.7547$ **(b)** $\cos x = -0.7547$.

2 You are given that $\sin 23° = 0.3907$.
Draw the graph of $y = \sin x$ for $0° \leqslant x \leqslant 360°$ and use it to find values of x in this range for which
   (a) $\sin x = 0.3907$ **(b)** $\sin x = -0.3907$.

3 Draw the graph of $y = \cos x$ for $0° \leqslant x \leqslant 360°$.
   (a) Given that $\cos 28° = 0.8829$, state another value of x in the range $0°$ to $360°$ for which $\cos x = 0.8829$.
   (b) On the same axes, draw the graph of $y = \cos 2x$.
   (c) Hence, solve, for values of x in the range $0° \leqslant x \leqslant 360°$,
      (i) $\cos 2x = 0.8829$
      (ii) $\cos 2x = -0.8829$

Mixed Exercise

1 $f(x) = 2x^2 - x + 1$
   (a) Find the value of **(i)** $f(3)$ **(ii)** $f(-2)$ **(iii)** $f(0)$.
   (b) Find the values of x for which **(i)** $f(x) = 92$ **(ii)** $f(x) = 37$.

2 Write down the equation of the graph that can be obtained from the graph of $y = x^2$ by a translation of:
   (a) $\begin{pmatrix} 0 \\ 3 \end{pmatrix}$ **(b)** $\begin{pmatrix} 7 \\ 0 \end{pmatrix}$ **(c)** $\begin{pmatrix} -2 \\ 0 \end{pmatrix}$ **(d)** $\begin{pmatrix} 0 \\ -3 \end{pmatrix}$

3 Describe the transformation that maps $y = x^2$ onto each of these graphs.
   (a) $y = 5x^2$ **(b)** $y = (5x)^2$ **(c)** $y = \frac{1}{5}x^2$ **(d)** $y = \left(\frac{1}{5}x\right)^2$

4 Draw the graph of $y = x^2 + 3x$ for $0 \leqslant x \leqslant 3$.
   (a) Reflect $y = x^2 + 3x$ in the x-axis and write the equation of the reflected graph in its simplest form.
   (b) Repeat part **(a)** but this time reflecting $y = x^2 + 3x$ in the y-axis.

5 Show how the graph of $y = x^2$ can be transformed into each of these graphs, illustrating your answers with a sketch graph.
   (a) $y = 2(x - 3)^2 + 1$ **(b)** $y = 3(x - 5)^2 - 4$ **(c)** $y = -2(x + 3)^2 + 5$

6 Draw the graph of $y = \sin x$ for $0° \leqslant x \leqslant 360°$.

    (a) Given that $\sin 52° = 0.7880$, state another value of x in the range $0°$ to $360°$ for which $\sin x = 0.7880$.

    (b) On the same axes, draw the graph of $y = \sin 2x$.

    (c) Hence, solve the equations

        (i) $\sin 2x = 0.7880$ **(ii)** $\sin 2x = -0.7880$

        for values of x in the range $0° \leqslant x \leqslant 360°$.

Checklist

You should know how to...	Grade	For more help, look back at Student Book pages...
transform graphs by means of translations parallel to the x- and y-axes	A*	524–526
transform graphs by means of one-way stretches parallel to the x- and y-axes	A*	526–528
reflect graphs in the x- and y-axes	A*	528–530
complete the square, then apply appropriate transformations	A*	531–536
transform trigonometric graphs of $y = \sin x$ and $y = \cos x$ and use their symmetry properties to solve trigonometric equations.	A*	536–540

30 Vectors

Exercise 30i

Links: 30A

What you should know

A vector can be represented by a directed line segment. The length indicates the magnitude of the vector, and the direction indicates the direction of the vector.

Vectors can be multiplied by scalars (numbers).

1 $\mathbf{a} = \begin{pmatrix} 3 \\ 4 \end{pmatrix}$ $\mathbf{b} = \begin{pmatrix} -2 \\ 2 \end{pmatrix}$ $\mathbf{c} = \begin{pmatrix} -1 \\ 3 \end{pmatrix}$

(a) Draw these vectors on a square grid.

$\mathbf{a}$ $\mathbf{b}$ $\mathbf{c}$ $\frac{1}{2}\mathbf{a}$ $-\mathbf{b}$ $-2\mathbf{c}$

(b) Write these as column vectors.

$-5\mathbf{a}$ $1\frac{1}{2}\mathbf{b}$ $4\mathbf{c}$

Exercise 30ii

Links: 30B

What you should know

Vectors can be added and subtracted using the parallelogram law.

$\overrightarrow{OP} = \overrightarrow{OA} + \overrightarrow{AP} = \mathbf{a} + \mathbf{b}$

$\overrightarrow{BA} = \overrightarrow{BO} + \overrightarrow{OA} = -\mathbf{b} + \mathbf{a} = \mathbf{a} - \mathbf{b}$

$\overrightarrow{AB} = \overrightarrow{AO} + \overrightarrow{OB} = -\mathbf{a} + \mathbf{b} = \mathbf{b} - \mathbf{a}$

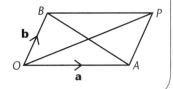

1 $\mathbf{d} = \begin{pmatrix} -2 \\ 1 \end{pmatrix}$ $\mathbf{e} = \begin{pmatrix} 4 \\ -1 \end{pmatrix}$ $\mathbf{f} = \begin{pmatrix} -3 \\ 5 \end{pmatrix}$

(a) Write these as column vectors.

$\mathbf{d} + \mathbf{f}$ $\mathbf{e} - \mathbf{d}$ $3\mathbf{d} + \mathbf{e}$
$2\mathbf{f} - 4\mathbf{d}$ $2\mathbf{d} - 3\mathbf{e} - 5\mathbf{f}$ $\mathbf{d} - \mathbf{e} + \mathbf{f}$

(b) On a square grid, draw diagrams to illustrate these vectors.

$\mathbf{e} + \mathbf{f}$ $\mathbf{d} - \mathbf{f}$ $\mathbf{f} - 3\mathbf{d}$ $2\mathbf{d} - \mathbf{f} - \mathbf{e}$

Exercise 30iii

Links: 30C

What you should know

A vector that starts at the origin is known as a position vector.

|OA| is called the modulus of OA and is the notation used to represent the magnitude of a vector.

1 Draw a separate diagram for each of these position vectors.
   Find the magnitude and direction (with the positive x-axis) of
   each position vector.

   (a) $\begin{pmatrix} 3 \\ 2 \end{pmatrix}$ (b) $\begin{pmatrix} 5 \\ -1 \end{pmatrix}$ (c) $\begin{pmatrix} -2 \\ 6 \end{pmatrix}$

   (d) $\begin{pmatrix} -7 \\ -4 \end{pmatrix}$ (e) $\begin{pmatrix} 6.5 \\ -3.5 \end{pmatrix}$

2 The diagram shows a grid of congruent parallelograms.
   The origin is labelled O and the position vectors of
   points X and Y are given by $OX = \mathbf{x}$ and $OY = \mathbf{y}$.
   Write, in terms of $\mathbf{x}$ and $\mathbf{y}$

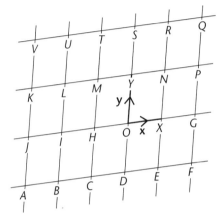

   (a) $\overrightarrow{OS}$ (b) $\overrightarrow{OJ}$ (c) $\overrightarrow{LA}$ (d) $\overrightarrow{VN}$

   (e) $\overrightarrow{QK}$ (f) $\overrightarrow{BT}$ (g) $\overrightarrow{EV}$ (h) $\overrightarrow{LR}$

3 Use the parallelogram grid for Question 2 to answer the following.
   (a) Write down the position vector equal to $-2\mathbf{x} + \mathbf{y}$.
   (b) Write down three other vectors equal to $-2\mathbf{x} + \mathbf{y}$.
   (c) Write down three vectors parallel to $\overrightarrow{DQ}$.
   (d) Write down three vectors that are half the size of $\overrightarrow{HR}$ and in
       the opposite direction.
   (e) Write down the vectors $\overrightarrow{AH}$ and $\overrightarrow{AN}$.
       Explain what this tells you about the points A, H and N.

4 Use the parallelogram grid for Question 2 to answer the following.

   Describe the position of these points if they were to be put on
   the parallelogram grid.

   For example, if $\overrightarrow{OA_1} = -\mathbf{x} + 1\frac{1}{2}\mathbf{y}$, A_1 would lie mid-way between
   M and T (see diagram).

   (a) B_1 if $\overrightarrow{OB_1} = \mathbf{x} + 1\frac{1}{2}\mathbf{y}$

   (b) C_1 if $\overrightarrow{OC_1} = -2\mathbf{x} + \frac{1}{2}\mathbf{y}$

   (c) D_1 if $\overrightarrow{OD_1} = 2\mathbf{x} - \frac{1}{2}\mathbf{y}$

   (d) E_1 if $\overrightarrow{OE_1} = -2\frac{1}{2}\mathbf{x} + 2\mathbf{y}$

   (e) F_1 if $\overrightarrow{OF_1} = -1\frac{1}{2}\mathbf{x} - \frac{1}{2}\mathbf{y}$

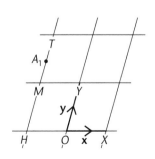

Exercise 30iv

Links: 30D

What you should know

The rules for the addition and subtraction of vectors and the multiplication of a vector by a scalar are the key elements of questions on vector geometry.

Remember that when vectors are equal they are equal in two ways – their lengths are equal and they have the same direction.

1 In this diagram $\overrightarrow{OA} = \mathbf{a}$ and $\overrightarrow{OB} = \mathbf{b}$.
   B and C are points of trisection of OE.
   A is the mid-point of OF.
   D is the mid-point of EF.
   Find these vectors in terms of $\mathbf{a}$ and $\mathbf{b}$, simplifying your answers.

   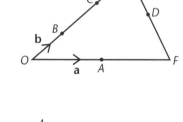

   (a) $\overrightarrow{OE}$ (b) $\overrightarrow{CE}$ (c) $\overrightarrow{FO}$ (d) $\overrightarrow{FE}$
   (e) $\overrightarrow{AE}$ (f) $\overrightarrow{BF}$ (g) $\overrightarrow{OD}$ (h) $\overrightarrow{CD}$

2 $OACB$ is a trapezium with BC parallel to OA and three times longer.
   M is the mid-point of AC. N is the mid-point of BC.
   $\overrightarrow{OA} = \mathbf{a}$ and $\overrightarrow{OB} = \mathbf{b}$

   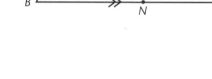

   Write down these vectors in terms of $\mathbf{a}$ and $\mathbf{b}$, simplifying your answers.

   (a) $\overrightarrow{BC}$ (b) $\overrightarrow{NC}$ (c) $\overrightarrow{NA}$ (d) $\overrightarrow{AC}$
   (e) $\overrightarrow{AM}$ (f) $\overrightarrow{OM}$ (g) $\overrightarrow{BM}$ (h) $\overrightarrow{MN}$

3 $ABCD$ is a trapezium with AB parallel to DC.
   $\overrightarrow{DA} = -3\mathbf{a} + 2\mathbf{b}$, $\overrightarrow{DB} = -2\mathbf{a} + 5\mathbf{b}$

   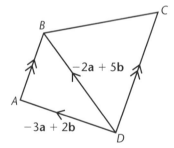

   (a) Find $\overrightarrow{AB}$ in terms of $\mathbf{a}$ and $\mathbf{b}$, simplifying your answer.
   (b) $\overrightarrow{BC} = k\mathbf{a} + 4\mathbf{b}$ (where k is a number to be determined).
       Find $\overrightarrow{DC}$ in terms of a, b and k and hence work out the value of k.

4 In this diagram, O is the origin and P, Q, R and S are the points with position vectors
   $\overrightarrow{OP} = -4\mathbf{a} + 7\mathbf{b}$ $\overrightarrow{OQ} = -2\mathbf{a} + 11\mathbf{b}$
   $\overrightarrow{OR} = 7\mathbf{a} + 5\mathbf{b}$ $\overrightarrow{OS} = 2\mathbf{a} + 3\mathbf{b}$

   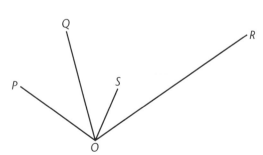

   Prove that $PQRS$ is a trapezium.

5 In the diagram, $\overrightarrow{OA} = \mathbf{a}$ and $\overrightarrow{OB} = \mathbf{b}$.

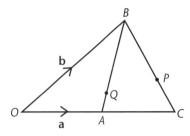

A is the mid-point of OC.

Q lies on AB such that $AQ : QB = 1 : 4$.

P lies on CB such that $CP : PB = 1 : 2$.

(a) Find these vectors in terms of $\mathbf{a}$ and $\mathbf{b}$, giving your answers in their simplest form.

    (i) $\overrightarrow{CB}$ **(ii)** $\overrightarrow{OP}$ **(iii)** $\overrightarrow{AB}$ **(iv)** $\overrightarrow{OQ}$

(b) Explain clearly the relationship between the points O, Q and P.

Mixed Exercise

1 $\mathbf{a} = \begin{pmatrix} 2 \\ 3 \end{pmatrix}$ $\mathbf{b} = \begin{pmatrix} -4 \\ 1 \end{pmatrix}$ $\mathbf{c} = \begin{pmatrix} 2 \\ -3 \end{pmatrix}$

(a) Draw these vectors on a square grid: $\mathbf{a}$, $\mathbf{b}$, $-2\mathbf{c}$, $2\mathbf{b} + \mathbf{c}$ and $\mathbf{b} - \mathbf{a}$.

(b) Write these as column vectors: $2\mathbf{a}$, $\mathbf{b} + \mathbf{c}$, $2\mathbf{b} - \mathbf{a}$ and $3\mathbf{a} - 2\mathbf{c}$.

2 In this diagram, O is the origin and OAB is a triangle in which $\overrightarrow{OA} = 3\mathbf{a}$ and $\overrightarrow{OB} = 4\mathbf{b}$.

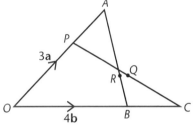

OB is extended to C such that $OB : BC = 2 : 1$.

P lies on OA such that $OP : PA = 2 : 1$.

Q is the mid-point of PC.

R lies on BA such that $BR : RA = 1 : 2$.

By finding the position vectors of Q and R, or otherwise, determine whether Q and R are the same point.

You must show your working, clearly stating your conclusion.

Checklist

You should know about...	Grade	For more help, look back at Student Book pages...
vector notation	A	508–511
adding and subtracting vectors	A	511–512
position vectors	A	513–519
vector geometry.	A/A*	519–521

31 Proof

Exercise 31i

Links: 31A

> **What you should know**
>
> Verify means to check something is true by substituting numbers into an expression or formula. It is a practical demonstration.
>
> Proof means to show something is true using logical reasoning.

1 p is an odd number and q is an even number.
Explain why:
  (a) $p^2 + 3pq$ is always an odd number
  (b) $(p + 7)(q + 4)$ is always an even number
  (c) $p^2 + q^3$ is always an odd number
  (d) $(p + q)^2 - (p + q)$ is always an even number
  (e) $(p - q)^3 - pq + 1$ is always an even number.

2 Explain why the sum of four consecutive odd numbers is always a multiple of 8.

Exercise 31ii

Links: 31B

> **What you should know**
>
> To prove by counter example, find one example where the stated result does not work.

1 m is an integer greater than 1.
Tom says that $m^3 + m$ is always a multiple of 10.
Give an example to show that Tom is wrong.

2 x is a whole number.
Ann says that $3x^2 - 2$ is never a prime number.
Give a counter example to show that she is wrong.

3 n is a positive integer less than 10.
Mark says that $n^2 + n^3$ is never divisible by 14.
Give an example to show that he is wrong.

4 k is a whole number such that $k \geqslant 3$.
Amir says that the value of $k^2 + 2k + 1$ is always a square number but never a cube number.
Give a counter example to show that he is wrong.

5 w is a prime number such that $5 \leqslant w \leqslant 13$.
y is an integer such that $6 \leqslant y \leqslant 10$.
Lauren says that $y^2 - w$ is never a multiple of 10.
Give an example to show that she is wrong.

Exercise 31iii

Links: 31C

> ## What you should know
>
> Geometrical proofs are done using step-by-step, logical reasoning.

1 $PQRS$ is a quadrilateral.
A line through P parallel to QR meets SR at T.
If angle PSR = angle QRS, prove that triangle PST is isosceles.

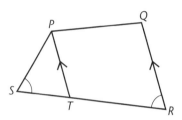

Exercise 31iv

Links: 31D

> ## What you should know
>
> The four conditions for triangles being congruent are: SSS   SAS   ASA/SAA   RHS

1 Triangle PQR is isosceles with $PQ = PR$.
M is a point on QR such that PM is perpendicular to QR.

Prove that triangles PQM and PRM are congruent.

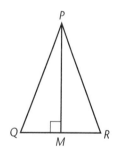

2 In the diagram, AB is parallel to DE
and $AC = CE$.
Prove that $BC = CD$.

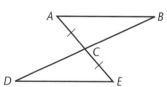

3 In the diagram, triangle UVW is isosceles with $UV = UW$.
S and T are points on UV and UW such that angle USW = angle UTV.
Prove that triangles SVW and TWV are congruent.

4 In the diagram, *AD* is parallel to *EF*, and *AB* = *CD*.
Triangle *REF* is isosceles with *RE* = *RF*.
Prove that **(a)** triangle *ARD* is isosceles
(b) triangles *AFC* and *DEB* are congruent.

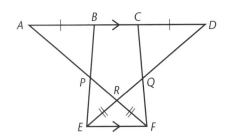

Exercise 31v

Links: 31E

What you should know

Verify means to check something is true by substituting numbers into an expression or formula. It is a practical demonstration.

Proof means to show something is true using logical reasoning.

1 Here is a rectangular grid of numbers in which a 3 × 2 rectangle is highlighted.

1	2	3	4	5	6
7	8	**9**	**10**	**11**	12
13	14	**15**	**16**	**17**	18
19	20	21	22	23	24
25	26	27	28	29	30

(a) In this 3 × 2 rectangle, work out
(i) bottom left × top right
(ii) top left × bottom right
(iii) the difference between the two answers.

(b) Try this for two more 3 × 2 rectangles.
What do you notice?

(c) *Prove* that the result will be the same for any 3 × 2 rectangle taken from the grid.

2 *A*, *B*, *C* and *D* are four consecutive integers.
(a) Verify that $(B + D)^2 - (A + C)^2 = 4(A + D)$ for any four consecutive integers of your choice.
(b) *Prove* that $(B + D)^2 - (A + C)^2 = 4(A + D)$ for any four consecutive integers.

3 A Fibonacci sequence is formed by adding together the previous two terms to get the next term.
So, starting with 2 and 5, the sequence will be 2, 5, 7, 12, 19, 31, ...
(a) For any four consecutive terms e.g. 2, 5, 7 and 12, work out
(1st term × 4th term) − (2nd term × 3rd term).
(b) Try this again for at least two more groups of four consecutive terms. What do you notice?
(c) Repeat parts (a) and (b) for the Fibonacci sequence 3, 7, 10, 17, 27, 44, ... What do you notice?
(d) Let the first term of a Fibonacci sequence = *a* and the second term = *b*.
(i) Write down the first six terms of the Fibonacci sequence in terms of *a* and *b*.
(ii) *Prove* the general result that you found in parts (b) and (c).

156

Mixed Exercise

1 x is an odd number and y is an even number such that $x > y$.
Explain why $(x - y)^2 + 5xy$ is always an odd number.

2 p, q and r are consecutive integers.
Will $(p + r)^2 - q^2$ be odd, even or can it be either?
Explain your answer.

3 n is an integer.
Pavel says that the value of $(n + 1)^3 - 4n$ is never a square number.
Give a counter example to show that he is wrong.

4 In the diagram, $ABCD$ and $CEFG$ are squares.
Prove that $DG = BE$.

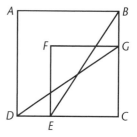

5 A, B, C, D and E are five consecutive integers.
  (a) Verify that $(A + C + E)^2 - (B + D)^2 = 5C^2$ for any five consecutive integers of your choice.
  (b) *Prove* that $(A + C + E)^2 - (B + D)^2 = 5C^2$ for any five consecutive integers.

Checklist

You should know how to ...	Grade	For more help, look back at Student Book pages...
verify and prove that a statement is true	D/C	558–560
use proof by counter example to show a statement is not true	D/C	561–562
prove geometrical results	C/B	563
prove results using congruent triangles	A/A*	563–566
prove results using algebraic manipulation.	A/A*	567–568